Arnold Foundation Monographs
XVI

# ARNOLD FOUNDATION MONOGRAPHS

I. THE POLITICS OF JUDICIAL REVIEW, 1937-1957: A Symposium, by T. C. Sinclair, Samuel Krislov, and Lloyd M. Wells, $1.00.

II. INTERNATIONAL INVOLVEMENTS IN THE MIDDLE EAST: A Symposium, by Paul Geren, John Paul Duncan, Robert F. Smith, Edward Taborsky, and Harold Karan Jacobson, $1.00.

III. THE PROBLEM OF GOVERNMENT IN METROPOLITAN AREAS: A Symposium, by Lee S. Greene, John G. Grumm, Frederick C. Irion, J. Lee Rodgers, and W. E. Benton, $1.00.

IV. POLITICAL AND SOCIAL PROBLEMS OF PUBLIC ADMINISTRATION IN UNDERDEVELOPED AREAS: A Symposium, by Oliver Benson, Lee S. Greene, Gholam H. Razi, and August O. Spain. $1.00.

V. FORMAL AND INFORMAL STRUCTURES IN STATE POLITICAL PARTIES: A Symposium, by Bancroft Henderson, James H. McCrocklin, nad Kenneth N. Vines, $1.00.

VI. PERSONAL RIGHTS AND LIBERTIES by T. C. Sinclair and Werner F. Grunbaum, $1.00.

VII. SUFFRAGE AND ELECTIONS by W. E. Benton, $1.00.

VIII. MUNICIPAL AND COUNTY GOVERNMENTS by J. William Davis and William E. Oden, $1.00.
POLITICAL SCIENCE IN A UNIVERSITY: A Lecture by Emmette S. Redford, $1.00.

IX. CASE STUDIES IN LATIN AMERICAN POLITICS by Cecil E. Johnson and August O. Spain, $1.00.

X. TEXAS CONSTITUTIONAL REVISION: THE LEGISLATIVE BRANCH by Mary Evelyn Huey, $1.00.

XI. MAN AND SPACE: Politics, Law, Organization by Rita Taubenfeld and Howard J. Taubenfeld, $1.00.

XII. MATHEMATICAL APPLICATIONS IN POLITICAL SCIENCE. A Symposium, by S. Sidney Ulmer, Harold Guetzkow, William H. Riker, and Donald E. Stokes, $1.00.

XIII. LEGISLATIVE REDISTRICTING IN TEXAS by Luther G. Haggard, Jr., Samuel B. Hamlett, and August O. Spain, $1.00.

XIV. BRIDGES EAST AND WEST by Senator J. W. Fulbright, $1.00.

XV. THE 1964 PRESIDENTIAL ELECTIONS IN THE SOUTHWEST by August O. Spain, Joseph L. Bernd, John W. Wood, Marvin Harder, George C. Roberts, and Kenneth N. Vines.

XVI. MATHEMATICAL APPLICATIONS IN POLITICAL SCIENCE, II, by Hayward R. Alker, Jr., Richard L. Merritt, Carl F. Kossack, Frank S. Scalora, Gerald H. Kramer, William H. Riker, and Otto A. Davis and Melvin Hinich. Joseph L. Bernd, Editor.

*Other titles in preparation*

# Mathematical Applications in Political Science, II

EDITED BY

## JOSEPH L. BERND

---

## ARNOLD FOUNDATION MONOGRAPHS XVI

---

*Published 1966 by*

THE ARNOLD FOUNDATION

JOHN M. CLAUNCH, Director

Southern Methodist University

Dallas, Texas

Copyright © 1966 by

Arnold Foundation of Southern Methodist University

# Foreword

The seven papers in this volume were originally presented at the second of two summer conferences on "Mathematical Applications in Political Science" held at Southern Methodist University, July 19-29, 1964* and July 18-August 7, 1965. To further the interdisciplinary design of the second conference, four papers were solicited from political scientists and three from scholars in other disciplines. Contributors from political science are Hayward R. Alker, Jr. and Richard L. Merritt of Yale University and Gerald Kramer and William H. Riker of the University of Rochester. Other contributors are Otto A. Davis (economist) and Melvin Hinich (statistician), Carnegie Institute of Technology, Carl F. Kossack (computer statistician) formerly of the Graduate Research Center of the Southwest and now of the University of Georgia, and Frank S. Scalora (mathematician) IBM-World Trade Corporation.

These conferences, sponsored by the NATIONAL SCIENCE FOUNDATION, were conceived to assist political scientists in learning how mathematical applications may be effectively utilized in their discipline. The meetings were designed to afford opportunities for the presentation of techniques and models involving statistical and mathematical applications and for high level discussions devoted to determination of the limits and validity of these relatively advanced concepts as utilized in political science.

---

* The two conferences were conceived and directed by Joseph Laurence Bernd. For the four published papers of the 1964 conference, see John M. Claunch (ed.), *Mathematical Applications in Political Science* (Dallas: Arnold Foundation Monographs: Southern Methodist University, 1965). Contributors are: Harold D. Guetzkow, William H. Riker, Donald F. Stokes, and S. Sidney Ulmer.

# Acknowledgments

The co-operation of a number of persons at Southern Methodist University has made possible this publication. Dean of the Graduate School Claude C. Albritton arranged for publication in concert with Allen Maxwell, Director of the S.M.U. Press, and John M. Claunch, Director of the Arnold Foundation. Paul D. Minton, Chairman, Department of Statistics, furnished valuable technical assistance, as did Mrs. Margaret L. Hartley, Editor of the S.M.U. Press. Martin Reese and the Printing Department were very co-operative.

Elsewhere, Evron M. Kirkpatrick, Executive Director of the American Political Science Association, must be credited for his successful efforts to initiate communication between the political science community and the National Science Foundation. N.S.F. sponsorship of two summer conferences in political science at Southern Methodist University inspired this publication. Special thanks for valuable ideas are due Reinhard Korgen and C. Russell Phelps of N.S.F. and Harold E. Way of Union College. Philip L. Martin, Political Science, Virginia Polytechnic Institute, read parts of the manuscript and offered suggestions. Ruth Bernd read the entire manuscript in early draft and contributed to the details of revision. Typing assistance was furnished by Mrs. Janice Johnson and Mrs. Annette Gilmore. As editor, I am solely responsible for any deficiencies in the conception and execution of the work.

Joseph L. Bernd

October 22, 1965

# Contents

Acknowledgments . . . . . . . . . . . . . . vii

Foreword . . . . . . . . . . . . . . . . . v

1. Solutions To Methodological Problems
   Introductory Note . . . . . . . . . . . . . 3

   Hayward R. Alker, Jr., "Causal Inference and
   Political Analysis" . . . . . . . . . . . . 7

   Richard L. Merritt, "The Representational Model
   in Cross-National Content Analysis" . . . . . . . 44

2. Statistical Techniques
   Introductory Note . . . . . . . . . . . . . 75

   Carl F. Kossack, "Statistical Analysis, the Computer,
   and Political Science Research" . . . . . . . . 77

3. Applications to Practical Politics
   Introductory Note . . . . . . . . . . . . . 109

   Frank S. Scalora, "Stochastic Models in the
   Behavioral Sciences: Applications to
   Elections and Advertising" . . . . . . . . . 111

   Gerald H. Kramer, "A Decision-Theoretic Analysis
   of a Problem in Political Campaigning" . . . . . 137

4. Models of the Political System
   Introductory Note . . . . . . . . . . . . . 163

   William H. Riker, "A New Proof of
   the Size Principle" . . . . . . . . . . . . 167

   Otto A. Davis and Melvin Hinich, "A Mathematical
   Model of Policy Formation in a Democratic
   Society" . . . . . . . . . . . . . . . . 175

# 1. Solutions to Methodological Problems

# 1. Solutions to Methodological Problems

## Introductory Note

*It would be surprising if the use of mathematics in any new field were spectacularly successful and encompassing from the outset.*
*—Oskar Morgenstern*

In its inception, a few devotees of the new science of politics appear to have assumed that the magic of numbers, like Athene, springing full grown from the head of Zeus, would solve all problems of measurement, causation and correlative relationship. (These persons might have observed that in economics and psychology subjective hypothesizing is still in order, although the subjective element has been *reduced* and precision *enhanced* through the use of mathematics.) The leap of faith, substituting mathematics and mechanistic models for older dogmas as the objects of faith, implies a misunderstanding of the significance of their enterprise. Mathematical models, properly employed, offer the advantages of precision in definition, identification, and communication. They are not the be-all and the end-all of scientific inquiry. Subjective human agency is still relevant and essential in conceiving and formulating, identifying and analyzing, but in certain important aspects of the process this agency and its attendant biases may be reduced or removed.

Given the exorbitant expectations of a few bemused devotees, groping for the essentials of the new science, it is not surprising that other scholars, initially dubious, accepted the contrast between optimistic expectations and subsequent paltry achievements as conclusive evidence that the entire operation was a hopeless and permanent failure. Mathematical applications to politics (the horseless carriage of the social sciences) is merely a fad (and will never replace Old Dobbin), they declared. In fairness it must be conceded that some of the studies (certainly not all, or most) seem to justify harsh conclusions: superficial ecological correlations, addition of the nonadditive, models requiring unobtainable data, or other equally slipshod procedures were exhibited.

It is easy to write off and consign to oblivion a new system, if one bases his conclusion on the obsolescent data of the earliest, and often halting and confused, period of development. This fallacy of premature rejection is readily detectable when hindsight is applied to most human endeavors. Imagine what a reviewer might say, for instance, in freshly applying today's sophisticated philosophical and methodological standards to the works of Kepler or Bodin. Yet these early scholars, with all of their limits and defects, were obviously important precursors of future contributions to the understanding of the cosmos and of man.

The French military command in the thirties was correct, on the basis of the available data of 1917 and 1918, in dismissing the strategic value of aircraft and in doubting the ability of the tank to pierce strong, static fortifications. Their monumental miscalculations were rooted in a reliance on obsolescent data, in a failure to anticipate technical improvements in the design of aircraft and tanks, and in their neglecting to keep pace with the effective integration of these weapons into offensive military systems. Is it possible that some critics of the new political science are prone to rely on obsolescent data and hyperbolic claims, drawn from the earliest stage and the least worthy disciples of the school?

Andrew Hacker, in calling for the abandonment of "the hope that political analysis can be either objective or scientific," may be correct, if "objectivity" and "science" are defined in the narrowest sense. Hacker's fallacy, in calling for a return to "subjectivity" (Does he mean to glorify the concept and rest contented with the shopworn status quo ante?) may be due to a failure to perceive how scientific processes evolve. Let us suggest an alternative to Hacker's policy, more realistic in the light of scholarly history and current developments:[1]

Let each student of politics follow the bent of his own tastes. Some will wish to remain subjective, including those who despair of being otherwise, or even those who prefer to be as subjective as possible. Others with the training and inclination will wish to join the quest for means of limiting subjectivity in the study of politics, rather than exulting in it. William H. Riker, observing the progress of economics, as an empirical science, one hundred and twenty years after the birth of Alfred Marshall, suggests that

---

[1] See Andrew Hacker, "Mathematics and Political Science" in James C. Charlesworth (ed.), *Mathematics and the Social Sciences* (Philadelphia: The American Academy of Political and Social Science, 1963), pp. 58-76.

A thoughtful and piercing review of Hacker's article has been written by Arthur S. Goldberg. See *American Political Science Review*, Vol. LVIII, 3 (September, 1964), pp. 684-685.

the example of economics is relevant. "[It] is somewhat premature to forego the scientific enterprise [in studying politics]."

The article by Hayward R. Alker, Jr. in this volume may well be an example of the kind of scholarship which enables a youthful scientific school to rise above the level of the fumbling and inchoate. The article reveals its author's skill in mathematics and statistics, as well as in political science, and he faces squarely the difficult questions which arise from both directions. Moreover, he brings to the study a refreshing awareness of relevant literature in several sister social sciences. It can scarcely be charged that the paper addresses itself to the trivial. The centrality of the question of causation in empirical social science research is obvious.

No doubt more will need to be said about the techniques of discovering and analyzing casual inference, but this article, in analyzing hierarchical and reciprocal concepts of causation, has achieved a maturity of temper and a sureness in handling intricacies which deserve emulation.

*Content analysis* is a technique for developing systematic information about a body of raw data—a newspaper, for example—in order to derive useful inferences about the values and perceptions of those who produced the raw data or those who were influenced by it. In a very loose sense, of course, historians have been engaged in content analysis since the first document was examined and the first inference was drawn. The term "content analysis," therefore, must be defined more precisely as a disciplined and quantitative study of contextual frequencies and associations, sometimes coded along attitudinal dimensions (such as "good-bad," "strong-weak," etc.). As developed by Lasswell, Pool, Stone, Merritt, and others, the systematized study and analysis of content has become scientifically precise by contrast with the largely intuitive and impressionistic procedures of the traditional historian.

Yet the problems of inference remain severe. Quantitative data drawn from the editorials of the *New York Times*, the *Frankfurter Allgemeine Zeitung*, or *Pravda*, for instance, are not self-evident indications of the values and perceptions of the publishers, the editors, or editorial writers, nor of the readership. Nor can we assume automatically that our analysis tells us what values the writers aimed to communicate to the readership. Editors do not customarily derive their editorials from quantitative models. Even if they employed the same model as the analyzers, there is no assurance that their interpretation of findings would be the same as that of the analyzers.

Despite problems of this nature, content analysis is a very necessary enterprise and one promising valuable returns. It is exceptionally important for informing policy-makers under modern conditions of international politics. To be sure, it would *appear* dispensable, if Dr. George Gallup and the Michigan Survey Research Center were accorded free access to opinion leaders in the Peoples' Republic of China or the U.S.S.R., or if the psychoanalyst who serves the editor of *Pravda* were in the pay of the C.I.A. This kind of information might appear most reliable, but we should want to check it through the use of other indicators, including those produced by content analytic techniques.

Since our survey researchers and psychoanalysts do not operate freely behind the Iron Curtain, and since the measurement and analysis of attitudes, perceptions, and values are delicate problems under the best of circumstances, content analysis remains a vital key to understanding opinion leaders and publics—past, present, and future. Its considerable importance, therefore, makes it vastly important that the enterprise be subjected to tough-minded scrutiny. This is the service performed by Richard Merritt in the article which follows. Merritt appraises his own field critically, and he offers thoughtful suggestions to guide further study.

# Causal Inference and Political Analysis*

## HAYWARD R. ALKER, JR.

*Yale University*

*If we can define the causal relation, we can define influence, power, or authority, and vice versa.*

—*Herbert Simon*[1]

If power is the ability more or less coercively to get people to do things that they otherwise would not do, exercising power is a special case of causation. Authoritative decision-makers legitimately cause the well-being or deference accorded to some members of a society to increase and the value positions of others to diminish. Thus political analysis, as we usually define it, may be thought of as the study of the processes and outcomes of authoritative and coercive social causation.[2] The causal agents range from individual citizens to national governments and international organizations; the arenas of their interaction include local communities, states, nations, and international societies.

Despite the centrality of causal inferences in political analysis, there has been a noticeable reluctance among political scientists explicitly to use causal language. Scholars would rather study "influence," or "power," or "decision-making," or "functional relationships," or "communication systems" than causal relationships per se, even though each of these concepts implies some kind of causal dependence of policy outcomes on decision-makers placed in varying sociocultural and political contexts.

A number of reasons may be offered for this reluctance. In academic discussions philosophical objections are frequently mentioned. Hume was the first but by no means the last skeptical

* In the preparation of this paper I was greatly aided by the thoughtful questions and computational assistance of Ronald Brunner. Hubert Blalock has offered a number of helpful suggestions. This research has been supported in part by the Yale Computer Center, The Yale Political Data Program, and Northwestern University's project on the Simulation of International Processes financed by JWGA/ARPA/NU (Advanced Research Projects Agency, SD 260).

[1] See reference *45* p. *5* in the Bibliography of this paper.

[2] The necessity and propriety of distinguishing social causation from merely physical or biological causation has been argued at some length by Sorokin and MacIver. (See references *40* and *46*). While accepting the reality of physical and biological determinism, this concept implies the necessity of including human perspectives and activities in our explanations of social, and in particular political, phenomena.

philosopher to note that we observe repeated associations rather than causal relationships. The meaning of causality to many such skeptics remains unclear. Operational methods for establishing causal relationships seem to be largely unknown.

Going beyond the objections of positivistic philosophers, perceptive students of political behavior have variously emphasized that politics involves reciprocal relationships between representatives and their constituencies, anticipated reactions of the strong and the weak, functional exchanges of leadership and support, and even negative feedback from the forces of nature to our political helmsmen. These scholars do not so much object to the use of causal language as doubt that causal theories about the complex interrelationships of political life can be either explicitly stated or empirically tested in a satisfactory fashion.

In addition to positivistic skeptics and doubting behavioralists, the critics of causal reasoning also include moralistic humanists. Doctrines of mechanistic causation and historical determinism are rejected as violating a fundamental belief in the freedom of the will. Even if the physical world is strictly determined, man's nature requires him to be both free and morally if not causally responsible for his actions.

Among the social sciences, political science has been especially sensitive to the complexities of human behavior and to the responsibilities of moral choice. In rejecting doctrines of economic determinism, class warfare, or psychological behaviorism, many political analysts have failed to learn of increasingly sophisticated and less objectionable treatments of the causal inference problem that have recently been proposed by economists, sociologists, psychologists, and other social scientists. This paper will review some of these developments, paying particular attention to the above-mentioned problems of operationally defining and testing causal relationships, modelling and testing reciprocal interactions, and somehow accommodating the doctrines of determinism and free will.

## I. Definitions of the Causal Relation

Objections to the Humean "constant conjunction" definition of causality can usually be interpreted as implying this definition's incompleteness rather than its incorrectness. After a brief review of some additions to and modifications of the Humean position, we shall present and discuss alternative mathematical treatments of the causal relation particularly appropriate for the social sciences.

A. *Components of the Causal Concept.*

*Asymmetry.* Perhaps the most fundamental implication of the Humean viewpoint is the *asymmetry of the causal relation.* A sergeant's command causes a private's response. The temporal asymmetry in this causal relation is clear as that between lightning and thunder—the cause comes before the effect. Also implied is a unidirectional relationship: if somehow we can get sergeants to issue certain commands, their privates will obey, but not vice versa. The temporal and/or directional asymmetry of causation has been widely emphasized in the writings of philosophers, statisticians, and social scientists.[3] It allows us to think of causal chains (*47*), (*28*), causal paths (*53*), causal funnels (*11*), causal hierarchies (*22, 45*), and even, in the more metaphysical formulations, of first causes and unmoved movers.

Political reality obviously includes a number of symmetrical, reciprocal influence relationships: for example, bargaining, the exchange of leadership for support, and arms races. If these can be studied from a causal point of view, a major difficulty in applying causal inference techniques to political phenomena will be overcome. Fortunately, several procedures have been developed for formalizing and testing causal models involving reciprocal relationships. A number of appropriate labels have been suggested: causal circles (*52*), reciprocal interaction (*55*), interdependent systems (*29, 34*), deviation amplifying feedback (*41*), and mutual causal processes (*17*). Since much of the rest of this paper will be devoted to illustrating some of these concepts, we only note here that all of these modelling techniques use the asymmetry idea in modelling reciprocal relationships, with or without assuming time lags between the initial and the feedback links.

*Contiguity.* In addition to the asymmetry of the causality concept, a good deal of the relevant philosophical and social science literature stresses the *contiguity of cause and effect.* Physicists have long talked about the idea of "no action at a distance" (*44,*

---

[3] For instance, see references *7, 12, 16, 21, 29, 33, 44.* Simon's notion of "unilateral couplings" and "causal orderings" among variables (*45*, Part I) correspond very closely, for example, to Deutsch's methods for establishing hierarchies in communication systems: "For our studies of communication . . . we might be very interested in getting operational tests for what is subordinate, what is coordinate, what is entirely separate. The test would be which feedback is coupled to the other asymmetrically" (*18*).

Chapter 4). Social scientists, at least those in the Lewinian tradition, have stressed that in order for sociological variables to cause behavior, they must enter into the psychological field of the individual (11, 46). Both natural and social scientists have rightly insisted that completely adequate explanations should specify the mechanisms linking causes to their effects, (e.g., reference 28).

Although there are difficulties with the contiguity assumption—contact between cause and effect seems always to be instantaneous—this emphasis has engendered a number of enlightening theories about specific links or pathways between natural or social causes and their effects. In an important paper, Miller and Stokes, for example, have compared the relative importance of congressmen's own beliefs about and perceptions of consistency opinions as influences on roll-call voting behavior (42). At several points below we also shall discuss the relative importance of alternative causal paths and mechanisms linking causes such as constituency opinions to their effects in the political arena.

*Lawfulness.* Herbert Feigl has suggested a "purified" definition of causality in terms of "predictability according to a set of laws" (21, p. 408). Even allowing for the uniqueness in some ways of every event, this definition makes explicit the need in causal inferences for comparable cases, multiple observations, and empirical generalizations. The existence of causal relations is in this sense nearly identical with the assumption—either metaphysical or methodological—of the uniformity of nature (see 32, Chapter 14 and the discussion of J. S. Mill in 44, Chapter 4). This definition thus makes more explicit the "theory-laden" nature of simple causal statements (28): sergeants' commands are obeyed because army traditions of authority are strong and because privates usually find the cost of noncompliance to be too high, etc. A number of other possibly different influences on behavior are also assumed to apply whenever we make even a simple causal argument.

This emphasis on empirical lawfulness helps to harmonize the mindlessness of the "constant or probable conjunction" view with more voluntaristic and humanistic outlooks.[4] In a recent critique of the Humean constant conjunction position, a British political philosopher, Alasdair MacIntyre, has argued:

---

[4] The Aristotelean view of causal laws can also be interpreted in both of these ways. For a statistical political example see the discussion and references in (2, pp. 3-5). The distinguishing of causal explanations from teleological, predictive, functional, and genetic ones will not be further undertaken here. (See, however, 32 and 44).

> . . . to look for the antecedents of an action is not to search for an in-
> variant causal connection, but to look for the available alternatives and
> to ask why the agent actualized one rather than another. . . . The ex-
> planation of a choice between alternatives is a matter of making clear
> what the agent's criterion was and why he made use of this criterion
> rather than another and to explain why the use of this criterion appears
> rational to those who invoke it. (*39*, p. 61).

To reconcile these two points of view we need first to stress that causal laws are not logically necessary or invariant but rather empirically observed constant conjunctions, such as commands and actions; secondly, we need to discover repeatedly invoked decisional criteria explaining observed responses. Some, but not all, causal arguments about human behavior do give such additional explanations in terms of expectations of undesired punishment, etc. Thirdly, we need to specify the historical context, constant or changing, within which such generalizations are expected to hold.

Some modes of causal explanation only implicitly explain why certain criteria of choice are used. In regression-like causal models, for example, undetermined coefficients represent choices of a particular criterion of action—each nonzero coefficient suggests the relevance of a particular variable, but the unspecified magnitude of the coefficient indicates a "degree of freedom" in the model. Voluntaristic and teleological explanations which plague many physical scientists (see *21, 40*), are both relevant and necessary to complete such explanations.

*Determinativeness.* A fourth connotation of the causation concept is frequently mentioned in the social science literature. Terminology such as "independent" and "dependent" variables (*33*), one variable "forcing" or "producing" changes in another (*7*), or the "manipulative" or "operational" significance of a causal equation (*45*) all strongly imply the determinativeness of the cause on the effect. In perhaps the most sophisticated recent statement of this point of view, Wold has suggested treating causal equations as "autonomous behavioral relationships" for different groups of actors in the economy (e.g., producers or consumers), giving the value of the "response" variable "conditionally expected" on the basis of known values of the "stimulus" variables and a *ceteris paribus* assumption about variables not explicitly included in the equation being discussed (*52*). This dependence of effect on cause is always seen as more than merely a statistical or logical asymmetric relationship. (6, 49, 51)[5]

Either out of modesty about attempting to mention all the causes involved or because of a basic belief that reality contains both deterministic and chance relationships, most physicists and social scientists no longer attempt to employ completely deterministic models. This liberation of causal thinking from an oversimplified and strongly mechanistic assumption has probably benefited social scientists even more than physicists. Multivariate (i.e., many-variabled) and stochastic (i.e., probabilistic) theories (see 7, 14, 34) have replaced many of the deterministic, single cause theories of the past (e.g., crude Marxism or Freudianism). As a result, in the mathematical formalizations of causal theory discussed below, the use of probabilistic or random terms will play an important part. So will the more modest goal of multiple causal explanations.

*Ceteris paribus.* Both the determinativeness and lawfulness of causal relations require a tentativeness about causal inferences that is sometimes overlooked. As empirical generalizations they can always be proved wrong by a sufficient number of counter-examples. Tentativeness concerning one's conclusions is also required because at some point one most *assume* that possibly confounding variables have been adequately controlled for. All concrete statements of causal relationships more or less explicitly make *ceteris paribus* assumptions.[6] An important consequence of this necessity is the need for caution about the extent to which

---

[5] Statisticians, for example, would distinguish sharply between a correlational and a causal interpretation of statistical coefficients like Goodman and Kruskal's tau or the slope of a linear regression. Both coefficients are asymmetrically, but not usually causally, interpreted. In addition, the causal viewpoint, unlike the merely "predictive" one, requires special attention to errors in the independent variables. (See 33, Chapter 29). Philosophers, on the other hand, are speaking both determinatively and asymmetrically when they refer to causes as important sufficient conditions. (See 44, p. 559 f).

[6] Besides the Wold usage illustrated above, definitions of the causal relation by Lazarsfeld, Blalock, and Simon have all stressed the tentativeness and falsifiability of causal claims in view of the *ceteris paribus* assumptions involved in concrete causal inference procedures. Thus Lazarsfeld, referring to universal and partial covariances between two attributes X and Y within subcategories of a test factor C, suggests that "if we have a relationship between X and Y, and if for any antecedent test factor [C], the partial relationships between X and Y do not disappear, then the original relationship should be called a causal one." (36, p. 146) Similarly, after assuming that "all other variables explicitly included in the causal model have been controlled or do not vary," Blalock says that "X is a direct cause of Y if and only if change in X produces a change in the mean value of Y." The list of other variables being controlled is limited to those explicitly included in the model, but Blalock must also assume that "the mean change in Y, for a given change in X is the same as the change that would always occur if all outside influences could be rigidly controlled." (7, p. 19)

model outcomes may be due to violations of these assumptions.

Historically, Ronald Fisher's work on randomization techniques has provided a number of systematic methods for experimentally isolating particular explanatory relationships. More recent work by sociologists and economists has focused on ways of being more sure about or relaxing the *ceteris paribus* assumptions themselves (5; 7, Chapter 5; 29; 52). Various of these techniques will be examined in some detail below.

## B. *Mathematizing the Causal Relation.*

When dealing with highly general scientific concepts, it helps to state them in a precise, abstract fashion capable of both logical and (when given a particular interpretation) empirical investigation. A more immediate reason for using mathematical formalizations of the causal relation is the extent to which previous formulations, from Aristotle on down, can better be understood by doing so. It then becomes clearer, for example, that logical necessity applies to the mathematical models rather than to the world they represent. Finally, the equation systems to be studied below make parsimonious, yet often plausible and testible assumptions about the asymmetry, contiguity, lawfulness, determinativeness, and *ceteris paribus* aspects of causal statements.

Following the econometric tradition (especially Wold, 52) we shall assume (1) that the causal laws relating members of a particular population can at least approximately be represented by linear, additive equations;[7] (2) that the philosophical belief in probabilism or partial determinism is adequately expressed by introducing "random" or "residual" terms in these equations, which themselves may be considered as empirically based generalizations about human behavior;[8] (3) that *ceteris paribus* assumptions will be stated as assumptions about these "random terms"; (4) that in each equation it will be possible to distinguish "independent"

---

[7] Threshold phenomena and multiplicative relationships are discussed in *1, 8, 14, 15*. Linear additive or multiplicative models with discrete time subscripts and random terms are very similar to some of the differential equation models used by Rapoport, Coleman, and others. They differ, however, to the extent that they include (1) only finite differences in variable values and change rates (rather than infinitesmal ones as in the calculus); and (2) random or error terms whose effects can more realistically change and cumulate from one time period to another.

[8] Economists often include in their models equations not susceptible to behavioral interpretations. The complicating implications of including definitional relations, etc., are discussed fully in (*29, 34, 50*).

from "dependent" variables,[9] with particular coefficients indicating
the magnitude of each causal link involved; and (5) that temporal
asymmetries may be indicated by $t$ subscripts on variables for the
different times at which they occur.

*Linear causal systems.* With these assumptions, we can represent any system of causally interrelated variables by a set of linear
equations like Equations (1a). These equations are assumed to
apply to all N members of some specified population:

$$X_1 + a_{12} X_2 + ... + a_{1G} X_G + b_{11} Z_1 + b_{12} Z_2 + ... + b_{1H} Z_H = U_1$$
$$a_{21} X_1 + X_2 + ... + a_{2G} X_G + b_{21} Z_1 + b_{22} Z_2 + ... + b_{2H} Z_H = U_2$$

$$. \tag{1a}$$

$$a_{G1} X_1 + a_{G2} X_2 + ... + X_G + b_{G1} Z_1 + b_{G2} Z_2 + ... + b_{GH} Z_H = U_G$$

Notationally, there are $G$ endogenous (mutually dependent) variables, denoted by $X$'s, and $H$ exogenous (independent or predetermined) variables, denoted by $Z$'s. It would be possible to have
various time subscripts on the $Z$'s; if desired the $Z$'s could even be
lagged values of the $X$'s, as when $Z_1 = X_{1(t-1)}$, $Z_2 = X_{2(t-1)}$, etc. We
shall assume that there are $G$ equations, each containing at least
one endogenous variable as well as other variables causally influencing the endogenous ones, in particular a random term $U$ and
possibly other exogenous variables. For simplicity of exposition, we
shall assume all the $X$'s, $Z$'s, and $U$'s to have expected (mean)
values of zero, and set the coefficient for one distinct endogenous
variable in each equation equal to unity.[10]

*Alternative simplifications.* In causal systems like (1a) each endogenous variable is determined by all other endogenous vari-

[9] In the econometric tradition, one may classify variables either in a single equation
or in a set of equations according to this kind of distinction. For a system of equations,
mutually dependent variables are called "endogenous" while those assumed to cause, but
not to be caused by, the endogenous variables are known as "predetermined" or
"exogenous" variables. It is sometimes useful to think of exogenous variables as those
that could be experimentally controlled, along with the residual terms, and the endogenous variables as those whose resulting variation we wish to examine.

[10] Using boldface letters to indicate matrices, we can succintly represent the causal
system (1a) either by the matrix equation (1b):
$$\mathbf{AX + BZ = U} \tag{1b}$$
or the even more compact form of equation (1c);
$$\mathbf{C\,Y = U}.$$
In these equations $\mathbf{A}$ and $\mathbf{B}$ are G x G and G x H coefficient matrices; X, Z, and U
are all G x 1 column vectors but also could be written as G x N matrices. $\mathbf{C}$ is a
G x G + H matrix composite of $\mathbf{A}$ and $\mathbf{B}$ while $\mathbf{Y}$ similarly contains G + H variables.

ables, all exogenous variables, and a random or residual term. If we are to assume the specific values of the $a$'s, $b$'s and $U$'s, to be unknown, we cannot estimate the magnitude of these terms without further assumptions relating either to the $U$'s or to the $a$'s and $b$'s. In designing models that are testable and whose parameters can be uniquely estimated, a number of further simplifications must therefore be made.

It turns out that choosing among alternative simplifications of linear stochastic systems involves us in a number of the conceptual controversies mentioned previously. The linear stochastic systems approach not only calls attention to these issues—some controversial decisions will have to be made before the model itself can be tested and its coefficients identified—it also allows us to state and argue the issues involved in a logical and empirical fashion.

These alternative choices of model-building assumptions can be arrayed along a number of dimensions. Specifically, for any multi-equation linear stochastic causal system, we must decide between:

1) *Hierarchical versus circular causation.* The basic idea of hierarchical causal relationships is that there exists a ranking of endogenous variables defined only in terms of other endogenous variables on which they are unilaterally dependent, and in terms of exogenous variables. In such a system the highest rank would be given to the first causes, the "unmoved movers" that depend only on exogenous variables and residual terms. Lower ranked endogenous variables are assumed to depend unilaterally only on higher ranked endogenous variables, exogenous variables, and residual terms. Because each variable is thus defined recursively (i.e., in terms of previously definable, higher ranked variables), such a set of equations is known as a *recursive system*. Because only unilateral dependencies occur in each equation of a recursive system (the dependent variable never "causes" the independent one) it is possible in an unambiguous way to estimate the coefficients of such an equation without taking other equations into account (see *51*, Chapter 2).

In fact, this simple decomposability of recursive systems into the behavioral regularities of autonomous (but partly determined) variables or actions is a major reason for the attractiveness of such models—it allows us to think about autonomous actors, and simply to describe their behavior. Another reason for the attractiveness of such models is their testability. Making additional assumptions about the residual terms, one can derive from competing recursive models a number of empirical predictions on the basis of which cne model can be chosen over another. This procedure will be illustrated in Section II below. Recursive, hierarchical models even allow for feedback relationships among endogenous variables *if* we assume such interactions take time. Then the endogenous variable being fedback also enters into our equations in an earlier, exogenous form.

If we feel reality or the approximate data that we can get from reality includes instantaneous feedback relationships, then a hierarchical rankings of endogenous variables is no longer possible. In this case all endogenous variables are not unilaterally dependent on logically prior variables. Estimating the coefficients of a single equation in such a relationship without taking the additional circularities into account gives us an incorrect picture of even the unidirection causal relationships that it contains (a mathematical illustration of this point based on work by Haavelmo is given by Valavanis in *50*, Chapter 4).

2) *Incomplete versus complete causal specification.* We can build models with or without exogenous variables. Recall that circular causal models appear to some as more realistic and to others as a practical convenience because good time specific data is not available. Similarly, the use of exogenous variables is thought by some to be more realistic and by others to be an unnecessary complication.

From a theoretical standpoint treating both endogenous and exogenous variables as "independent" causes in a recursive system seems an unnatural complication. Not identifying the causes of the exogenous variables also smacks of incompleteness. There are a number of reasons for including exogenous variables, however. For nonrecursive models, they can give us sufficiently distinct equations so that we somehow grasp ("control" or "manipulate" in a quasi-experimental sense) each equation separately and uniquely identify its coefficients using multiequation estimation techniques (*50*, Chapters 6, 9). For recursive models, they can give us a larger number of prediction for testing the models (as in *9* and *51*). For either recursive or non-recursive systems, by forcing us to make ourselves somewhat more specific about the other factors influencing the endogenous variables, we are reducing our dependence on possibly unrealistic assumptions about the residual terms.

3) *Uncorrelated versus correlated residual terms.* If residual

terms are uncorrelated, the causal system is assumed to be isolated to the extent that no outside variable effects more than one endogenous variable. As implied above, including exogenous variables can help make the "uncorrelated residuals" assumption more realistic. Fortunately the uncorrelated residuals assumption is a testable one—as the methods for choosing among causal models, noted below, illustrate.

If we drop the uncorrelated errors assumption, we are in a certain sense agreeing that causal systems cannot be as nearly isolated from reality as the uncorrelated residuals assumption implies. Imbedding our models to the extent that other variables might be assumed to cause residual changes in several of the endogenous variables is undoubtedly more realistic. Unfortunately, however, not assuming uncorrelated residuals mean that it is even harder uniquely to identify the equations of causal models.[11]

4) *Static versus dynamic models.* Whether or not we include explicit temporal asymmetries in our causal models is another major model building choice, capable of either philosophical or empirical argument. Econometricians more than sociologists, for example, have studied time-lagged relationships, probably because meaningful time units (e.g., fiscal years) and data have been more readily available. (Compare 29 and 34 with 7, 10, 14 and 42). Two other related issues are also involved: the problem of making longitudinally valid (time series) predictions from cross-sectionally gathered (simultaneous) data and the extent to which statistical models assume or imply social systems to be in equilibrium.[12]

A basic problem is how to interpret the coefficients or their estimates obtained from simultaneous models in which no time subscripts explicitly occur. Coleman argues, for example (14), that assumptions about uncorrelated residuals and unchanging model coefficients are in effect equivalent to assumptions that processes underlying simultaneous data are in equilibrium with each other. He also has shown that coefficients from cross-sectional analyses

---

[11] Some of Wold's most interesting work in implicit causal systems (52) concerns recursive models with correlated residual terms. Some such models give predictions equivalent to certain non-hierarchical systems. In order to make his models give determinate predictions, however, Wold has either to introduce exogenous terms or fail to identify some of the coefficients he employs. See also (53, 55).

[12] The cross-sectional versus longitudinal inference problem is discussed in a number of places. See, for example, (2, Chapter 5 and the references) and (50, Section 12.17). Coleman's work on the equilibrium interpretation of causal models is outstanding (14, Part II, and 15) and so is the wealth of material in the econometric literature (52, Section 2, and references).

have a simple longitudinal interpretation only when variable change rates are either negligible or constant (15). Perhaps the best we can say is that simultaneous results are more nearly causally interpretable in a longitudinal sense when re-equilibriating tendencies are quick and variable change rates are slow.[13]

*Mixing simplifying assumptions.* As implied above, different simplifying assumptions tend to go together. At one "extreme" there are those model builders (e.g., Blalock) who tend to use hierarchical causal relationships, no exogenous variables, uncorrelated error terms and temporal equilibrium; at the other "extreme" are those (e.g., Koopmans) who tend to assume circular causal relationships and correlated residual terms and use exogenous variables and time lagged equations. Obviously there are no simple ordering principles that will explain why the four major issues in model building have tended to produce these two extremes.

A certain underlying set of attitudes about the decomposability or the interdependence of social reality seems, however, to exist. The hierarchical modellers act *as if* they believe reality to be more decomposable. This would mean that unilateral dependencies are adequate for describing causal relationships in which changes are slow or negligible and that causal systems can be satisfactorily isolated from their environments. If the uncorrelated residuals assumption is not too bothersome, then we need not introduce exogenous variables.

The modellers of reciprocal, interdependent systems, on the other hand, may see reality as less decomposable and more dynamic. Simultaneous reciprocal dependencies would then seem natural, as well as outside influences on several of the endogenous variables. Exogenous variables, in this view, are necessary to help identify the coefficients of the reciprocal relationships among the dependent variables, as well as to reduce difficulties created by variables affecting the residual terms.

Perhaps a better organizing principle would be that the "hierarchical" modellers are at an earlier stage in theory-building. Bla-

---

[13] Econometricians usually make a number of additional assumptions that are also controversial, but will not be discussed here: (5) that the residual $U$'s have quasi-random, i.e. joint normal distributions, with zero means; (6) that the $U$'s are assumed not to be autocorrelated (i.e., correlated with previous values of themselves); (7) residual terms are also assumed to be uncorrelated with the explicit endogenous variables. (See 50, pp. 77-79). These assumptions are most useful when trying to estimate population parameters from sample statistics.

lock might argue, for example, that current data and theories don't suggest or allow more realistic and more complex, yet falsifiable, models. Certainly the statistics of recursive systems (least-squares analysis as compared to maximum likelihood methods) is much simpler than that of interdependent ones. This developmental perspective would also explain the greater concern with testing alternative theories to be found in the "hierarchical" literature and the increased attention to parameter estimation techniques by the modellers of interdependent systems.

Fortunately, a number of modelling approaches fall in between these two extremes. Blalock has recently discussed nonlinear models and is interested in dynamic systems (8); Boudon has recently dealt with parameter estimation problems in hierarchical, static models with correlated residual terms (10); Wold has introduced the idea of implicit causal models that are dynamic, allow correlated residual terms, but maintain hierarchical relationships among equations denoting behavioral regularities of autonomous actors (52).

## II. HIERARCHICAL CAUSAL RELATIONSHIPS

We shall illustrate both the simplicity and the attractiveness of the hierarchical modelling approach with several models drawn from Daniel Lerner's classic work on political development, *The Passing of Traditional Society* (37). Each of the linear stochastic models discussed will assume unilateral causal dependencies (recursive relationships), uncorrelated residual terms, and no explicit temporal asymmetries. Exogenous variables will not be employed in our estimating procedures nor considered as elements in paths linking causes to their effects.

Lerner states his thesis about the universal modernizing role of literacy and media development in several places and in several ways. At one point he refers to the chicken and egg problem of reciprocal causal relations (37, p. 56) and forsakes speculative causal inference problems for testable correlational ones. But then, he argues in almost hierarchical causal fashion:

> . . . the Western model of modernization exhibits certain components and sequences whose relevance is global. Everywhere, for example, increasing urbanization has tended to raise literacy; rising literacy has tended to increase media exposure; increasing media exposure has "gone

with" wider economic participation (per capita income) and political participation (voting). (37, p. 56).[14]

Only in the "gone with" link does he use language that is clearly correlational and not causal.

At another point (37, pp. 58-65), Lerner makes inferences from multiple correlations to three phase historical and causal sequences. Relations between stages, if not within them, also appear to be hierarchical (recursive and unilateral).

> Within [the] urban matrix develop both of the attributes which distinguish the next two phases—literacy and media growth. There is a close reciprocal relationship between these, for the literate develop the media which in turn spread literacy. But, historically, literacy performs the key function. . . . The capacity to read . . . equips [the population] to perform the varied tasks required in the modernizing society. Not until a third phase . . . does a society begin to produce newspapers, radio networks, and motion pictures on a massive scale. This, in turn, accelerates the spread of literacy. Out of this interaction develop those institutions of participation (e.g., voting) which we find in all advanced modern societies (37, p. 60).

*Mathematizing the causal relations.* Before presenting the causal models derived from Lerner's work, let us briefly mention the operational procedures used in measuring the variables we shall study. *Urbanization* will be measured by the percent of a nation's population living in cities of over 20,000 population size; *literacy* will also be a percentage measure: percent of population over age 15 that is literate as reported to UNESCO sources. *Media development* will be measured by a combined index (whose elements are highly intercorrelated) of media items; per capita radios, newspapers, telephones, etc. The *political participation* index is a weighted sum of voting turnout data and a measure of political enculturation (two indices of participation which themselves are rather distinctly intercorrelated).[15]

Let us now explicitly state several possible models implied by the Lerner quotations. Since he himself is quite explicit about

[14] W. D. Burnham has reminded me that American political development obviously does not fit this scheme; its high male political participation came before high media exposure and economic development. The Lerner model makes more sense in European and Afro-Asian contexts.

[15] References are given in Figure 1. It is clear that the operationalizations are at best tentative, especially since they are assumed to have interval scale validity. Some of the most profitable work on causal modelling in political science will obviously deal with variables that have lower levels of measurement. For a variety of causal models applicable to nominal scale data, see *14*, Chapters 4-6.

reciprocal linkages, our hierarchical models are obviously simplifications of his thinking, useful mainly for illustrating causal modelling procedures. Because all our data is from around the year 1960, we in addition must assume rather than prove the relevance of cross-sectional analysis procedures for longitudinal inference.

The simplest interpretation of the above quotes is a three-fold "stages of development" theory, in which urbanization brings about literacy, literacy then increases media development, which in turn increases political participation. By allowing only the developmental sequence of causal links above such an obviously oversimplified approach sounds something like a civics course (Emily Post version): come off the farm, learn to read, read the newspapers, and then vote wisely. Mathematically, this theory may be represented by equations (2a) and (2b):

$$
\begin{aligned}
X_1 &= U_1 \\
a_{21}X_1 + X_2 &= U_2 \\
a_{32}X_2 + X_3 &= U_3 \\
a_{43}X_3 + X_4 &= U_4
\end{aligned}
\tag{2a}
$$

$$\Sigma U_1 U_2 = \Sigma U_1 U_3 = \Sigma U_1 U_4 = \Sigma U_2 U_3 = \Sigma U_2 U_4 = \Sigma U_3 U_4 = 0 \tag{2b}$$

In these equations $X_1$ indicates urbanization, $X_2$ literacy, $X_3$ media development, $X_4$ political participation; and $U_1$, $U_2$, $U_3$, $U_4$ are the corresponding residual causes, which are assumed to be uncorrelated. In system (2a), $X_1$ is the "dependent" variable in the first equation, $X_2$ depends on $X_1$ and $U_2$ as indicated by the second equation, etc. An arrow scheme representation of this "simple stages theory" is given in Figure 1.A.

FIGURE 1. Three Causal Theories of National Political
Participation Levels.* (N=85)

A. *Simple Stages Theory*
Urbanization ($X_1$)
↓
Literacy ($X_2$)
↓
Media
Development ($X_3$)
↓
Political
Participation ($X_4$)

| Deductions | Predictions | Results |
|---|---|---|
| $b_{13.2}=0$ | $r_{13}=r_{12}r_{23}$ | .41 vs. $(.70)(.58)=.41$ |
| $b_{24.3}=0$ | $r_{24}=r_{23}r_{34}$ | .66 vs. $(.58)(.42)=.24$ |
| $b_{14.23}=0$ | $r_{14}=r_{12}r_{23}r_{34}$ | .42 vs. $(.70)(.41)(.42)=.12$ |

## B. *Lerner Theory*

Urbanization $(X_1)$

Literacy $(X_2)$ $\longrightarrow$ Media Development $(X_3)$

Political
Participation $(X_4)$

| Deduction | Prediction |
|---|---|
| $b_{14.23}=0$ | $r_{14}=r_{12}r_{24}+\dfrac{(r_{34}-r_{24}r_{23})(r_{13}-r_{12}r_{23})}{1-r_{23}^2}$ |

Results

$$.42 \text{ vs. } (.70)(.66)+$$
$$\frac{[.42-(.66)(.58)][.41-(.70)(.58)]}{1-(.58)(.58)}=.46$$

## C. *Revised Lerner Theory*

Urbanization $(X_1)$

Literacy $(X_2)$ $\longrightarrow$ Media Development $(X_3)$

Political
Participation $(X_4)$

| Deductions | Predictions | Results |
|---|---|---|
| $b_{13.2}=0$ | $r_{13}=r_{12}r_{23}$ | .41 vs. .41 |
| $b_{14.23}=0$ | $r_{14}=r_{12}r_{24}+\dfrac{(r_{34}-r_{24}r_{23})(r_{13}-r_{12}r_{23})}{1-r_{23}^2}$ | .42 vs .46 |

* Data on urbanization and literacy are from Russett, Alker, Deutsch, Lasswell, *World Handbook of Political and Social Indicators* (New Haven: Yale University Press, 1964). Media Development is a factor index based on per capita radio, newspapers, telephones, and other data derived from the *World Handbook* and other sources. Political participation data comes from Alker and Hopkins, reference 3. Basic ingredients are *World Handbook* data on percentage voting turnout and Banks and Textor data on political enculturation (*The Cross-Polity Survey* [Cambridge: M.I.T. Press, 1963]).

A much more realistic theory for explaining high levels of national political participation is given in Figure 1B. As represented there, and in Equations (3a) and (3b) below, this "Lerner theory" suggests the urban situation $(X_1)$ as a cause of both literacy $(X_2)$ and media development $(X_3)$, with literacy rather than the media playing the "key role" in the obviously reciprocal relationship between media producers and consumers. Out of the interaction of both of these develop higher levels of mass political participation $(X_4)$. Note again how in each equation the "dependent" variable on the left of the equals sign is distinguished by its coefficient of unity.

$$X_1 \qquad\qquad\qquad\qquad\quad = U_1$$
$$a_{21}X_1 + \quad X_2 \qquad\qquad\quad = U_2$$
$$a_{31}X_1 + a_{32}X_2 + \quad X_3 \qquad = U_3 \qquad\qquad (3a)$$
$$a_{42}X_2 + a_{43}X_3 + X_4 = U_4$$
$$\Sigma U_i U_j = 0 \quad (i, j = 1, \ldots, 4; i \neq j) \qquad\qquad (3b)$$

As before, we are assuming in Equations (3b) that other things are equal—that residual influences on $X_1$, $X_2$, $X_3$ and $X_4$ are uncorrelated with each other.

It is interesting to compare causal systems (2a,b) and (3a,b) with the general (indeterminate) model (1a). The new models have been restricted in several ways. Besides the obvious omission of exogenous variables and the "uncorrelated" residuals assumption, a subtler difference concerns the pattern of linkage or dependence coefficients, the $a$'s. A sufficiently large number of $a$'s have been assumed to equal zero[16] so that *it is possible to arrange all the remaining a coefficients into a triangular pattern* (the X and $a$ subscripts were in fact chosen so that this would occur). In a geometric sense, this kind of coefficient "pyramid" corresponds exactly to the set of recursive relations that characterize hierarchical causal systems. In Equations (2a) and (3a), $X_1$ is the first cause, literacy the second cause, and media the third. Each variable is caused only by random influences and other variables higher in the causal hierarchy. Figures 1A and 1B also suggest visually the same pyramid of unilateral causal dependencies.[17]

*Choosing among causal models.* The tentativeness of all scientific arguments, in particular causal ones, means that at best we will fail to reject one or several after submitting them to the test of

[16] Other simplifying assumptions such as linear equations relating the $a$'s, could also have been made (see 34). These restrictions, however, would probably violate the present assumption of hierarchical causal relationships.

[17] A third model, obtained by setting $a_{31}$ in Model (3a) equal to zero (Lerner at one point omits this link), is given in Figure 1c. It will be discussed in more detail in the next section of this paper.

experience. To test the hierarchical theories in Figure 1, we need to make deductions from their mathematical models, which (when empirically reinterpreted) we may match with observed relationships.

At least two equivalent strategies for making deductions from the models of systems (2a,b) and (3a,b) are possible (a third is described in footnote 20). First of all, we can multiply together pairs of equations in either model (e.g., 2a), average these products over all members of the population being studied, divide these products on both sides of the equals signs by appropriate standard deviations, and then set the $\Sigma U_i U_j$ products equal to zero because of assumptions (2b) and (3b). These equations can then be solved for the values of the $a_{ij}$'s in terms only of observable variances and correlations; if enough $a_{ij}$ terms have been set to zero (more than $C\ (4,2)=6$ in the present examples), additional predictions among observable correlation coefficients will also be found. For more extended applications of this method the reader is referred to (45, Chapter 2; 2, Chapter 6; and 10).

A second, simpler and more elegant approach is suggested in (7, Chapter 3 and 51, Chapter 2). Since the equations of hierarchical causal models are autonomous behavioral relations, by assumption the "dependent" endogenous variable in each equation depends solely on the independent variables in that same equation and whatever variables these independent variables themselves depend on. Therefore, we can legitimately estimate by least squares or some other method the coefficients of any single equation in hierarchical models with uncorrelated random terms without taking the other equations explicitly into account. More precisely, *the partial slopes corresponding to missing a coefficients within the coefficient pyramid should always be zero if we control for all other variables of higher causal order.* Variables of higher causal order are those in higher rows of the coefficient pyramid.

Turning to the models in Figure 1, this rule means that three partial slopes in Theory A, one partial slope in Theory B, and two partial slopes in Theory C should be zero. (These logical deductions from the causal model are given on the left below each of the arrow diagrams in Figure 1). When partial slopes equal zero, corresponding partial correlations are also zero; therefore we can transform these deductions into the simplified "predictions" concerning observable correlations given in the figure. (Formulas for higher order partial stops and correlations are obtainable from many statistics books.) These predictions can be verified to be exactly the same as those made by the "multiplying equation pairs" method described above.

Looking at the results of our analysis, the comparisons between the values of the expressions on either side of the prediction equations, we see first that one prediction of the "simple stages theory" is exactly correct, but that two others are way off. The Lerner theory, on the other hand, was one result that is within 0.04 of being correct, a difference between correlations that could easily be attributed to sampling (or measurement) error.[18] The "Lerner Theory," in which direct causal links between urbanization and media development and between literacy and political participation are added to the links of the simple stages theory, thus better survives our limited empirical test.

A "revised Lerner Theory" as shown in Figure 1.C., however, is also plausible. This theory omits a direct link between urbanization and media development; as such it is a compromise between the "simple stages theory" and the original "Lerner Theory." Like the latter of these theories, it too resists falsification. Whether or not the revised theory is preferred to the original theory depends on such additional criteria as parsimony and realism.

*Estimating causal links and causal paths.* Considering the number of assumptions and operational approximations involved in attempting to test a longitudinal theory with cross-sectional data, the successful survival of the Lerner Theory is gratifying enough for us to proceed to estimate the magnitude of the links involved.[19] Especially interesting, once the a's are known, would be some idea of the magnitude of the various pathways linking urbanization to political participation.

For the original "Lerner Theory" (Figure 1.B), we shall calculate both dependence and path coefficients. By "dependence coefficients" we mean standardized *a* coefficients in causally interpreted linear stochastic models; "path coefficients" are *products*

---

[18] Sampling and measurement error problems in causal modelling are as yet not thoroughly explored. (See 7 and 33, however, for some interesting beginnings). For recursive models it seems reasonable to expect that significance tests of the magnitude of supposedly zero partial slopes would be feasible if the appropriate sampling, equal variance, and normality assumptions are satisfied.

[19] The "stages theory" is only one of several other "plausible" three, four, and five arrow theories from which predictions were made that turned out to be incorrect. Since several other less plausible models make the same predictions as the (revised) theory, additional criteria for choosing among them are required.

of dependence coefficients along particular chains linking a causal variable to one of its effects (see Wright's extensive development of these ideas in 53, 54, 55, and Boudon's applications in 9, 10).[20]

Dependence coefficients for the Lerner Theory were calculated by separate least squares regression analysis of each equation in system (3a). Table 1 gives these and related path coefficients. As we might expect from the good predictions of the Revised Lerner Theory, the urbanization → media link is weak; so is that between media and participation. A more challenging (but debatable) inference concerns the relative strength of two pathways from urbanization to participation: urbanization → literacy → participation and the urbanization → literacy → media → participation. Going causally from literacy to participation seems to characterize modernization processes more than the more indirect route through media development.

Since our data downgrade the causal role of the media in direct contradiction to the emphasis in Lerner's writings, a partial analysis of other correlation data (using the same causal model) was attempted to see whether or not measurement error in the media index was responsible. The subsequent analysis indeed showed the media → participation link to be stronger and the literacy → participation one to be weaker.

---

[20] Wright's basic formula in the case of no correlated error terms is: "Any correlation between variables in a network of sequential relations can be analyzed into contributions from all the paths (direct or through common factors [causes]) by which the two variables are connected, such that the value of each contribution is the product of the coefficients pertaining to the elementary paths." (53, p. 163). Applying this rule to the arrow model of Figure 1B gives six equations, assuming $a$'s to be for standardized variables:

$$r_{12} = a_{21}$$
$$r_{13} = a_{31} + a_{21} a_{32}$$
$$r_{14} = a_{21} r_{42} + a_{21} a_{32} a_{43} + a_{31} a_{43}$$
$$r_{23} = a_{32} + a_{21} a_{31} \qquad (3c)$$
$$r_{24} = a_{42} + a_{32} a_{43} + a_{21} a_{43} a_{31}$$
$$r_{34} = a_{43} + a_{32} a_{42} + a_{31} a_{21} a_{42}$$

These equations can be manipulated to give the same prediction ($r_{14.23} = 0$) given by the first and second derivation methods already discussed. They are in fact the same equations derivable by the "multiplying equations" method when the variables and coefficients involved are standardized, but this time obtained by inspection of the arrow diagram! Wright also gives a rule for writing down prediction and estimation equations when ultimate factors (those depending only on random terms) are correlated. (53, p.163 f). Both of these rules are stated on the assumption that dependent variables are on the opposite side of an equals sign from independent ones (this is not true for 3a). Therefore in comparing results among different derivation procedures all $a$ coefficients in 3c should each individually be preceded by a minus sign.

TABLE 1. Least-Squares Estimates of Standardized Dependence and Path Coefficients for the Lerner Theory of Modernization* (N=85)

| Dependent Variable | Independent Variable | Dependence Coefficient $(a_{ij})$ |
|---|---|---|
| Literacy $(X_2)$ | Urbanization $(X_1)$ | $a_{21}=0.70$ |
| Media $(X_3)$ | Urbanization $(X_1)$ | $a_{31}=0.063$ |
| Media $(X_3)$ | Literacy $(X_2)$ | $a_{32}=0.57$ |
| Participation $(X_4)$ | Literacy $(X_2)$ | $a_{42}=0.64$ |
| Participation $(X_4)$ | Media $(X_3)$ | $a_{43}=0.051$ |

| Dependent Variable | Causal Path | Path Coefficient |
|---|---|---|
| Participation $(X_4)$ | $X_1 \rightarrow X_2 \rightarrow X_4$ | $P_{124}=a_{21}a_{42}=0.45$ |
| Participation $(X_4)$ | $X_1 \rightarrow X_2 \rightarrow X_3 \rightarrow X_4$ | $P_{1234}=a_{21}a_{32}a_{43}=0.02$ |
| Participation $(X_4)$ | $X_1 \rightarrow X_3 \rightarrow X_4$ | $P_{134}=a_{31}a_{43}=0.003$ |

* Estimates are derived by the least squares method applied to the model (3 a,b) and data of Figure 1B. They are equivalent to estimates derivable from the path coefficient approach and Equations (3c) using the observed correlational values $r_{12} = .70$, $r_{13} = .41$, $r_{14} = .42$, $r_{23} = .58$, $r_{24} = .67$, $r_{34} = .42$. The path coefficients in the table add to 0.47, indicating an error of 0.05 from the true value of their sum ($r_{14} = .42$) if the model were exactly correct. It should also be noted that, unlike the convention of equations 1a, 2a, and 3a, positive dependence coefficients refer to positive dependence relationships.

## III. RECIPROCAL CAUSAL RELATIONSHIPS

In testing the model and estimating the parameters in the Lerner Theory, we had to remove any direct reciprocal ($\underset{\leftarrow}{\rightarrow}$) links between two variables in order to get determinative results. Such links are a special case of non-hierarchical circular or feedback influence relationships. To illustrate a theory building procedure not restricted to the assumptions of uncorrelated random terms and hierarchical relationships, but including exogenous variables as influences on the endogenous ones, we shall consider another set of propositions regarding national systems.[21]

Our method of theorizing will, however, be different from the Lerner example in that interrelated propositions will be derived from the interaction between traditional conceptions of political alternatives and more empirically based data analysis. It is hoped

[21] We shall still have to assume that our findings indicate something like longitudinal (historical) causal relationships. All our equations may still be interpreted as probabilistic behavioral generalizations (or laws), but they will no longer be assumed to indicate autonomous relationships. Because of the high level of aggregation in dealing with national systems, it will also be even more difficult than it was in the previous examples to identify specific actors, or within-nation mechanisms responsible for each of the causal links involved. Nonetheless we shall sometimes refer to people in either illustration in such terms as "media consumers and producers," "voters," etc., when these terms seem appropriate.

that this one small example will illustrate how many of the insights of the rich qualitative tradition can be partially translated into more mundane, but more precise and testable, theories about crucial reciprocal political relationships.[22]

In particular, we shall attempt to state, test, and estimate parameters for several theories about reciprocal relationships between communism and democracy in economically developed Western societies.[23] Other mutually dependent variables will include levels of executive stability, political participation, and domestic group violence; each will be assumed exogenously and partially to depend on levels of urbanization, literacy, and economic development and other residual factors.

Sources for the indicators to be used, and correlations among them, are given in Table 2. Endogenous, political indicators include: 1) *Communist voting* as a percentage of national totals (Yale Political Data Program, etc.); 2) *polyarchy* (approximately as coded by Arthur Banks on the basis of the existence of a legitimate opposition, free press, elections, etc.); 3) *domestic group violence* (logged deaths as a fraction of population size, according to Rudolph Rummel); 4) *political participation* (as described in the notes to Figure 1, primarily an index based on voting turnout) and 5) average *executive stability* or tenure (approximately as coded by the Yale Political Data Program). *Literacy rates, urbanization* and *percapita Gross National Product* are the exogenous variables. Symbolic labels for the endogenous $(X_1, \ldots, X_5)$ and the exogenous variables $(Z_1, Z_2, Z_3)$ are given in the margins of the table.

[22] The possibility of applying such models to "exchange" and "feedback" relationships such as consumer-producer exchanges has already been mentioned (see *17, 18, 19, 45, 52*). Similarly, Lerner presents a "circular" arrow model for the relationships among interest articulation, interest aggregation, and public communication, etc. (*38*, p. 348 ff) based on work of Almond and Coleman; he also discusses changes in the "vicious circle" of poverty necessary to bring about a "growth cycle" (*38*, p. 346 ff). Maruyama has reinterpreted Myrdal's work on the growing gap between rich and poor nations (e.g., *43*), in terms of deviation amplifying reciprocal causation (*41*). Literary commentators on politics also often stress cyclical relations: Sartre, for example, has emphasized how the oppression of the colons and the hatred of the colonial reinforce each other (see references in *20*).

[23] Several of these clearly do not apply to Soviet Bloc countries or non-communist underdeveloped ones. Thus these theories will be more modest in their generality than those which Lerner claimed were valid "regardless of variations in race, color, creed" (*37*, p. 46). That some political (perhaps more than socioeconomic) "laws" differ in different contexts has been amply demonstrated. Ways of formulating (usually non-additive) causal theories that encompass such varieties have been discussed in (*1, 14, 15*, and the references cited therein).

TABLE 2: Correlations Among 3 Socioeconomic and 5 Political Characteristics of 36 Economically Advanced Non-Communist Nations*

| | $X_1$ | $X_2$ | $X_3$ | $X_4$ | $X_5$ | $Z_1$ | $Z_2$ | $Z_3$ |
|---|---|---|---|---|---|---|---|---|
| Communist Vote ($X_1$) | 1.00 | .217 | −.087 | .170 | −.251 | .179 | −.172 | .008 |
| Polyarchy ($X_2$) | | 1.00 | .639 | −.608 | .193 | .487 | .215 | .594 |
| Political Particip'n. ($X_3$) | | | 1.00 | −.535 | .526 | .769 | .389 | .641 |
| Domestic Group Violence ($X_4$) | | | | 1.00 | −.392 | −.463 | −.230 | −.440 |
| Executive Stability ($X_5$) | | | | | 1.00 | .469 | .402 | .507 |
| Literacy ($Z_1$) | | | | | | 1.00 | .488 | .670 |
| Urbanization ($Z_2$) | | | | | | | 1.00 | .468 |
| Per Capita GNP ($Z_3$) | | | | | | | | 1.00 |

* Nations all have per capita Gross National Products above $250.00. Socioeconomic indicators are taken from B. Russett, H. Alker, K. Deutsch, H. Lasswell, *World Handbook of Political and Social Indicators* (Yale University Press, New Haven: 1964); political ones are factor indices derived in reference 3 and discussed in the text of the present paper.

*Mathematizing reciprocal causal relationships.* A circular arrow diagram and an equivalent non-pyramidal system of reciprocal linear stochastic causal relationships are presented in Figure 2. *The heart of this theory is the assumption that communist voting ($X_1$) and polyarchy ($X_2$) are antithetical to each other.* While domestic group violence ($X_4$) breeds communist voters (because of the frustration it represents or causes), highly polyarchic systems are assumed to encourage legitimate participation ($X_3$) and to discourage or obviate domestic group violence. Legitimate participation (e.g., voting) is thought to reduce the need for violence; communist voting is modelled as decreasing the chances of democratic government (polyarchy).

In a sense, these interrelated propositions follow from the "best" arguments of traditional apologists for both democracy and communism.[24] Communism is supposed to follow domestic revolution and violence and, in the long run, to bury democracy. Polyarchy, on the other hand, is said by its modern advocates to increase

[24] Models of this complexity do not spring full blown from correlation matrices like Table 1, even though they may be influenced by them. At first I tried hierarchically to take the "best case" arguments and put them together, with communist voting producing executive stability and high participation, and polyarchy decreasing violence and increasing participation. This didn't work, even when a link equivalent to the "communism will bury polyarchy" argument was added. Turning to reciprocal models, I was unsuccessful in several attempts meaningfully to include executive stability and still get a set of reasonable parameter estimates.

popular participation in government and to decrease the likelihood of domestic violence.

FIGURE 2: A Reciprocal Causal Theory of Equilibrium Relationships Between Communist Voting and Democratic Government in Economically Advanced Non-
Communist Nations.

### A. Arrow Diagram*

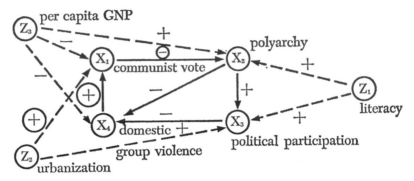

### B. Linear Model

| Endogenous Political Links | Exogenous Socioeconomic Links | |
|---|---|---|
| $X_1 \qquad\qquad + a_{14} X_4$ | $+ b_{12} Z_2 + b_{13} Z_3 = U_1$ | |
| $a_{21} X_1 + X_2$ | $+ b_{21} Z_1 \qquad + b_{23} Z_3 = U_2$ | (4a) |
| $a_{32} X_2 + \quad X_3$ | $+ b_{31} Z_1 + b_{32} Z_2 \qquad = U_3$ | |
| $a_{42} X_2 + a_{43} X_3 + \quad X_4$ | $+ b_{43} Z_3 = U_4$ | |

* Continuous signed arrows refer to predicted political relationships; signed dashed
arrows refer to predicted socioeconomic links. Circled signs above the arrows indicate
theoretical sign prediction was different from that of the estimate.

*Taken together these two points of view imply two potentially
unstable circular relationships between polyarchy and communist
voting,* one via domestic violence, the other via participation and
resulting changes in violence and communist voting. That an unstable equilibrium is implied by these interrelated propositions is
shown by assuming a random increase (or decrease) in communist voting. Following the arrow diagram, we see that chances
for polyarchy would decrease and, by both circular paths, violence
would increase, bringing more communist voters to the polls—
truly a vicious cycle because these voters would further decrease

the extent of the nation's democracy. An initial spurt for polyarchy, on the other hand, would probably end in a world of democracies if these propositions were correct!

TABLE 3: Estimated Dependence Coefficients for Original and Revised Equilibrium Theories of Communist Voting — Democratic Government Relationships*

| Variables | | Original Theory (Figure 2.A) | | Revised Theory (Figure 3.A) | |
|---|---|---|---|---|---|
| *Effect* | *Cause* | *Estimate†* | *Theory* | *Estimate†* | *Theory* |
| comm. vote | violence | $a_{14} = 1.30$ | X | $a_{14} = -.49$ | √ |
| polyarchy | comm. vote | $a_{21} = -.40$ | X | $a_{21} = -.40$ | √ |
| particip'n. | polyarchy | $a_{32} = -.45$ | √ | $a_{32} = -.20$ | √ |
| violence | polyarchy | $a_{42} = .17$ | √ | $a_{42} = .24$ | √ |
| violence | particip'n. | $a_{43} = .46$ | √ | $a_{43} = .39$ | √ |
| comm. vote | literacy | | | $b_{11} = -.57$ | √ |
| comm. vote | urbanz'n. | $b_{12} = .27$ | X | $b_{12} = .34$ | √ |
| comm. vote | income | $b_{13} = .44$ | √ | | |
| polyarchy | literacy | $b_{21} = -.04$ | √ | $b_{21} = -.04$ | √ |
| polyarchy | income | $b_{23} = -.57$ | √ | $b_{23} = -.57$ | √ |
| particip'n. | literacy | $b_{31} = -.53$ | √ | $b_{31} = -.58$ | √ |
| particip'n. | urbanz'n. | $b_{32} = -.02$ | √ | | |
| particip'n. | income | | | $b_{33} = -.13$ | √ |
| violence | income | $b_{43} = .05$ | √ | $b_{43} = .04$ | √ |

* Estimates were obtained by least-squares regression methods from the *reduced forms* of Equations (4a: Figure 2.A) and (5a: Figure 3A). The standardized regression coefficients in each case were the same. For dependent variables 1, 2, 3, and 4 (in that order) and exogenous variables 1, 2, 3 (in that order) they were: .42, —.32, —.12; .20, —.13, .52; .62, —.026, .24; —.32, .04,—.25. A mimeographed sheet describing the algebraic derivations involved is available from the author on request.

† If the relevant link in the arrow diagrams of Figure 2 and Figure 3 has a *plus* sign, this means the related *a* or *b* coefficient should be *minus*, and vice versa, because all the X's and Z's are on the same side of the equals sign.

Exogenous to these essentially political dependencies in Figure 2 are a number of socioeconomic links with urbanism, literacy, and percapita GNP. Since this theory does not attempt to explain the causes of these variables themselves, we were able to draw on the earlier hierarchical modelling experience of this paper in choosing specific exogenous relationships. Use was also made of the simple correlations in Table 1. Specifically, literacy was assumed to increase both polyarchy and popular political participation, urbanization (à la Lenin) to increase communist voting and political participation, and high per capita income to increase the chances of democracy, while decreasing the appeal of both violence and communist voting. This last trio of democratic "attributes" follows rather naturally, of course, from the work of Lipset and others on socioeconomic conditions for democracy.

After mathematically specifying a complex model of political and socioeconomic interrelationships, there remained the problem of assuring oneself of the identifiability of the parameters implied by the model. If from the empirical distributions of both exogenous and endogenous variables, a coefficient estimating procedure will always lead to a unique set of estimates, a model's equations are exactly identifiable.[25] The alternative situations are that a model is *overidentified* (several values of the *a*'s are predicted, or additional relations among correlations can be derived) or *underidentified* (in which case the model is indeterminate and we do not have enough information to obtain less than an infinitude of coefficient estimates). Fortunately, the variety of exogenous links used in the equations of the reciprocal causal models in Figures 2 and 3 is sufficient for each of these equations to be identified.[26]

Identifiability is thus a theoretical property that may hold independently of the data used to estimate, validate, or falsify causal models. Stating or revising one's causal models so that each equation will be identifiable is obviously an important theory building problem. Basically, for any question, other equations in the model

[25] This problem pertains to both hierarchical models (in which no uncorrelated residuals assumptions are made) and reciprocal ones. In general recursive models are identifiable only if uncorrelated residuals are assumed (see *10*). If we had added a direct causal arrow between urbanism and participation in the first version of the Lerner Theory (Figure 1B), no excess predictions could then have been derived from the model, although equations (3c) would still have given determinate results for the *a*'s. Adding one more causal link (and *a* coefficient) would have simultaneously made the Lerner Theory non-recursive and non-identifiable. Six equations in seven unknowns (the old *a*'s plus two new ones) would have allowed an infinite number of solutions for the values of these *a*'s. A good introduction to the identifiability problem may be obtained by reading (Hood and Koopmans, *29*, Chapter 2) and then (Valavanis, *50*, Chapter 6).

[26] Actually, we tested one model not presented here, with fewer *b* coefficients than those in Figures 2 or 3, that was "overidentified." It proved unsatisfactory.

Koopmans has stated that: "A *necessary* condition for the identifiability of a [behavioral] equation within a given linear model is that the number of variables excluded from the equation (more generally, the number of linear restrictions on the parameters of that equation) be at least equal to the number of [behavioral] equations, less one. . . . A *necessary and sufficient condition* for the identifiability of a [behavioral] equation within a linear model, restricted only by the exclusion of certain variables from certain equations, is that we can form at least one nonvanishing determinant of order G-1 out of these coefficients, properly arranged, with which the variables excluded from that . . . equation appear in the G-1 other . . . equations." (*29*, p. 38) Tintner (*48*, Chapter 7) gives a simple illustration of the application of these conditions.

have to be different enough from it so as not to be confused with it.

*Estimating and testing reciprocal models.* Because reciprocal models in general cannot be used to generate predicted relationships among observable correlation coefficients (*49*, Chapter 6), some other method is necessary for choosing among reciprocal causal models. The approach to be used here suggests eliminating or failing to eliminate reciprocal causal models primarily on the basis of correct or correctable theoretical predictions of the signs of estimated coefficients. Notice how in one sense we are pragmatically using a theory in order to test it; this approach has little payoff, of course, unless some a priori degree of belief can be generated concerning the direction of particular causal relationships.

Estimates of the *a*'s and *b*'s in Figure 2 could be obtained by a number of econometric methods, including maximum likelihood analysis. The one used here is generally referred to as a "sophisticated least-squares procedure."[27] It assumes that the equations of a causal model, e.g. Figure 2, implicitly rather than explicitly indicate behavioral relationships. To get at the implicit coefficient values requires taking the simultaneous circular causal effects of dependent variables on themselves into account. Therefore, all endogenous variables in a set of causal equations have simultaneously to be solved for in terms of the exogenous variables from which unbiased coefficient estimates may be obtained by least-squares procedures. Going *back* from "reduced form" least-squares estimates obtained from equations relating each X to only exogenous variables and random terms is, in fact, one of the prime reasons why the identifiability question is raised: can we derive unique values of the *a*'s and *b*'s from least-squares estimates based only on the reduced form equations? For identifiable equations, the answer is yes.

Turning now to Table 3 and Figure 2, we see that three coefficients ($a_{14}$, $a_{21}$, $b_{12}$) have had their signs incorrectly predicted. Looking at Figure 2, and changing in our mind the circled (in-

---

[27] The standardized coefficients were estimated by least squares analysis of the *reduced form* of the causal model of Equations (4a). This method allows for the interdependence of the X's, solving for them in terms of exogenous variables and residual terms. This "sophisticated least squares procedure" gets around the principal objections raised by maximum likelihood advocates. (See *50, 51* regarding this and other estimating procedures.) The present results were obtained by tedious algebraic derivations of the reduced forms of Equations (4a) and (5a), then computerized least squares analyses, and finally the calculation of the *a*'s and *b*'s in the unreduced equations using these results. A more elegant approach to getting the X's in reduced form is given by Equation (6), obtainable from Equation (1b) above:

$$\mathbf{X} = -\mathbf{A}^{-1}\mathbf{B}\mathbf{Z} + \mathbf{A}^{-1}\mathbf{U} \qquad (6)$$

correct) arrow signs, we see that our model signs now show a circular reinforcement of polyarchy by communist voting, via less domestic violence and more communist votes or via greater participation, less violence and again more communist votes. Unstable equilibrium is implied.

A careful reanalysis was necessary to see why the sophisticated least squares procedure produced estimates violating Figure 2's theoretical predictions. Trying, if possible, to keep the same number of missing exogenous variables in each of the model's equations—in order to retain the uniquely identifiable characteristic of the model, it was first decided to assume a positive impact of literacy on communist voting in line with similar effect already assumed for total voting levels in Figure 1. From the reduced form regression analysis, income seemed a less promising agent of decreased communist voting (decreasing *concentration* of wealth would have been better), so it was removed from this link and joined to public political participation. A weak link (urbanization → participation) was also dropped.

A close look at some particular cases (residuals analysis) helped suggest why two of the three wrong predictions had been incorrect (perhaps the third was due to improper specification of the exogenous relationships). First of all, $b_{12}$ is positive because the highest communist voting levels have occurred in countries like Finland, Italy, France, and Chile, none of which is terribly urbanized. *In Western Europe, communism appears to be more characteristically rural than urban,* as at least one leading Chinese theoretician would like us to believe. Similarly, $a_{14}$ is positive because these countries have average or above average polyarchy scores. Communist voting in Western Europe indeed occurs most significantly in countries tolerating radical opposition.[28] The existence of circa 15%–20% communist voting levels helps to maintain (or is "functional for") traditions and institutions tolerating dissent. Perhaps communist voters can legitimately relieve or outgrow the frustrations in this relatively harmless way. *Apparently, communist voting at these levels increases rather than diminishes system democracy.*

Testing of a revised "peaceful co-existence" reciprocal causal model (Figure 3) devised in light of this reanalysis gives more plausible size estimates for the *a* and *b* coefficients, as well as correct signs for each of the twelve propositions summarized in Table 3 under the Revised Theory heading.

FIGURE 3. A Revised Theory of Reciprocal Equilibrium Relationships Between Communist Voting and Democratic Government in Economically Advanced Non-Communist Nations.

## A. Arrow Diagram*

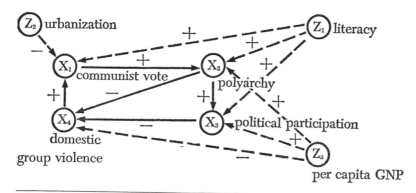

## B. Linear Model

Endogenous Political Links.     Exogenous Socioeconomic Links

$$
\begin{aligned}
X_1 \qquad\qquad\qquad & + a_{14} X_4 + b_{11} Z_1 + b_{12} Z_2 \qquad\quad = U_1 \\
a_{21} X_1 + \quad X_2 \qquad & \qquad\quad + b_{21} Z_1 \qquad\qquad + b_{23} Z_3 = U_2 \\
& \qquad\qquad\qquad\qquad\qquad\qquad\quad (5a) \\
a_{32} X_2 + \quad X_3 \qquad & \quad + b_{31} Z_1 \qquad\qquad + b_{33} Z_3 = U_3 \\
a_{42} X_2 + a_{43} X_3 + \quad X_4 \quad & \qquad\qquad\qquad\qquad + b_{43} Z_3 = U_4
\end{aligned}
$$

* Continuous signed arrows refer to predicted political relationships; signed dashed arrows refer to predicted socioeconomic links.

Comparing the signs and magnitudes of the various links of the revised communist voting-polyarchy theory, we see that the "viciousness" of the less polyarchy $\rightarrow$ more violence $\rightarrow$ more communist voting $\rightarrow$ less polyarchy circle has disappeared; it is no longer in unstable equilibrium. Both the three-arrow and five-arrow circles now have an *odd number of minus signs*, if one calculates path coefficients along these two routes. Negative net path coefficients indicate *negative feedback*, i.e., reequilibrating ten-

[28] See Allardt's paper (4) for details about the existence of rural and urban communism in Finland. A hierarchical model reversing the direction of the communist vote $\rightarrow$ polyarchy links gave unsatisfactory predictions. It should be quite clear, however, that our small sample size means sampling errors associated with choosing one model over another would be large in the present context.

dencies in political processes (see *15, 19, 54*) that are more consistent with our original assumptions about the longitudinal causal interpretability of cross-sectional analyses. Introducing time lags in relationships among these variables would then allow growth, equilibrium, or decay in such adjustment processes to occur.

## IV. Causation and Freedom

Determinism attracts the social scientist for a number of reasons. Causal agents are seen as unmoved movers, while causal laws order chaotic experience. Thus causal explanations go below surface relationships to determinative realities. But the use of partly deterministic causal models does not imply the absence of free choice, even within the deterministic parts of these theories. The real problem is the use of more or less coercive or irrational power: "The distinction between free choice and behavior that is compelled is drawn *within* the domain of causation. . . . A free choice is not uncaused, but one whose causes include in significant measuring the aspirations and knowledge of the actor who is choosing." (*32*, p. 121). There are no apparent a priori reasons why choices freely or rationally made should persistently fail to exhibit lawful regularities; the same possibilities should also exist for coerced or irrational choice. These regularities should *not*, however, be confused with the logical necessity of tautological mathematical relationships.[29]

Despite such arguments as these, mathematical models of political relationships for many political scientists continue to connote the restriction of freedom rather than the satisfaction of curiosity or opportunities for political development. It may therefore be of value briefly to discuss the kinds of freedom assumed or implied in the mathematical models and causal theories discussed in previous sections of this paper.

*Political Choices.* Unlike many of the recent quantitative studies of national political systems, the reciprocal theories of Part III above have stressed causal interdependence among *political* variables.[30] Levels of domestic group violence and political participation were seen both to depend on and to influence collective de-

---

[29] Detailed discussions of the causation-determinism issue as it applies to human behavior may be found in references *22, 32, 39, 40,* and *46.*

[30] The case for the autonomy of the political has been strongly put in Samuel Huntington's recent review of the cross-national literature on political development (*30*).

cisions concerning the desired forms of political institutions. Each of these variables can and should be thought of as representing observed regularities in partly autonomous collective political choices, more or less freely arrived at.

Even when a more realistic assessment of the importance of these mutually dependent links was made by taking into account several important exogenous variables, political decisions (measured by the *a* coefficients) were seen to be at least as determinative of political outcome as socioeconomic causation (measured by the *b*'s).[31]

*Residual or random causes.* In both the hierarchical and the reciprocal theories examined above, each dependent variable was assumed to be only probabilistically determined. The residual terms (symbolized by the *U*'s) indicated the lack of generality of each explanatory equation. If, as appears to be the case, the *U* terms account for roughly between 0 and 50 percent of the resultant political behavior,[32] here too are important indications of self-generated or even chance behavior. Except when domestic group violence is involved, these "random" phenomena need not be coercive ones.

*Variable dependence coefficients.* Besides the political choices and random terms, another aspect of freedom or indeterminacy in the above mathematical theories is the dependence coefficients themselves. They were not predicted on an a priori basis; rather, they were estimated from a particular set of data. As originally specified, the arrow models indicated the existence and possibly the direction of selected causal links. The sizes of the related dependence coefficients are estimated only after the relevant data on independent and dependent variables were collected. Because these findings are only descriptive of a particular set of data (and certainly not a random sample at that), other dependence coeffi-

[31] Herbert Simon has made much the same kind of argument including exogenous influences on presidential choices in making a more realistic assessment of presidential power: "If we regard the President as an 'independent variable,' then we arrive at one assessment of his influence. If we add to our system the environmental influences created by the administrative bureaucracy which greatly restricts the variability that differences in personal qualities and beliefs would otherwise produce . . . , we arrive at a smaller estimate of the influence of those personal qualities and beliefs." (45, p. 68)

[32] These rough estimates were derived from Figure 3 and Table 4. The squared multiple correlation coefficients ($R^2$'s) for the model's 4 reduced form equations indicate that approximately 15%, 40%, 25%, and 60% of the variation of their respective dependent variables was "predetermined" by socioeconomic variables. If the remaining variance is attributed about equally to political variables and also to random causes, the above 0 - 50% variance estimates are approximately correct.

cients consistent with the theories described are quite possible for different sets of data and different time periods. Granted that the choice of the degree of open competitiveness in national political systems is partly determined by a variety of other political and socioeconomic factors, changes in the relevant mix of these causal factors represent significant differences between various kinds of political systems.[33]

This means that such models can be used to define and measure structural changes associated with evolution or decay of political systems. Changes in the very "laws" governing social and political relationships are, in fact, some of the most frequent topics of concern in the classical literature of politics. Causal models may even be used to explain why such gradual or revolutionary breaks with the past have occurred!

*A multiplicity of empirically acceptable causal models.* As our analysis of the original and revised Lerner models suggested, more than one causal model may be consistent with a particular set of observed correlations. This may be true whatever the generality of the correlations concerned. Specifically, our procedure of rejecting or failing to reject particular causal theories never succeeded in eliminating all but one possible theory. At best several plausible theories were partly discounted.

Mathematically, it is easy to show that several causal theories make the same empirical predictions (the developmental sequence $X \to Y \to Z$ and the double causal situation $X \leftarrow Y \to Z$, for example, both imply that $r_{xz.y} = 0$). Since adding or subtracting variables and links from a model may or may not change the number or nature of predictions involved, both mathematical and methodological injunctions to be tentative in advocating the truth of one particular model coincide.

Theoretically, these possibilities allow for causal situations in which different but indistinguishable causal models are at work.

---

[33] The fact that the polyarchy-communism model gives several coefficient estimates with different signs when applied to economically underdeveloped nations is a graphic illustration of the more or less autonomous changes that developed nations have made in the determinants of the political characteristics, even if we assume the same arrow model (without signs) to apply.

In a similar vein, Talcott Parsons has frequently argued that an impressive achievement of most industrialized Western democracies has been the depolarization of the lower class—radicalism voting relationship. "Status polarization" of the 1956 American presidential election, for example, was almost completely avoided. These findings do not imply, of course, that other determinants of voting behavior did not exist. See the Parsons reference cited in *19* and the data in *11*.

Even within one causal model, there may be several pathways of change. Nonrecursive models of political competitiveness may in fact summarize and cover up two or more recursive explanatory models, each chosen by a number of national political systems.

*Determinism and freedom.* It should be clear that the incomplete specification of the causal models presented in this paper allows for a variety of choices and indeterminacies in the reality being described. In addition, the possibility has been suggested that political variables may themselves represent free and responsible collective political choices, some of whose partially determined consequences we have tried to explore. Philosophically, this perspective corresponds to the humanistic view that social reality is only partly predetermined. Mathematically, the procedures investigated have helped make explicit the variety and extent of the constraints and opportunities involved.

## V. Summary and Conclusions

Within the variety of possible explanations for political events, social causation focuses on generalizations with determinative significance. Causal statements are also usually asymmetric in character, pay attention to pathways of influence between causes and effects, and tentatively assume other possible causes are being safely ignored or controlled. All of these aspects of causal explanation apply to recent social science attempts to abstract and generalize relatively precise and comprehensive arguments using linear stochastic systems. It need not be assumed that these generalizations apply independently of the historical context from which they are drawn.

Within the causal modelling tradition there are again a variety of procedures for theoretically coping with segments of political reality. Many of them bear directly on philosophical arguments regarding the nature of social reality. Models may be dynamic or static, stochastic or deterministic, dealing either with what we have called hierarchical or reciprocal influence relations. Major alternatives also exist as to the extent of isolation we assume, *ceteris paribus*, regarding the systems of relationships being described. The price for logically insuring identifiable outcomes from a system of equations, whatever their degree of implied isolation, involves some additional specifications regarding the size or absence of some of the possible causal links, including possible links to exogenous variables whose causes themselves are not fully assumed. We choose among such alternatives for a number of theoretical and personal reasons, but their scientific survival depends on resistance to empirical falsification.

Within the causal modelling approach to political analysis there are a number of ways of accounting for human decisions and responsibilities. Whether freely or coercively arrived at, individual and collective choices can be considered as themselves causally responsible for other political consequences. Probabilistic models confess from the start that specific outcomes cannot be exactly predicted, even if certain tendencies are known to occur. Statistical models with unspecified but partly restricted coefficients reduce but do not eliminate the degrees of freedom associated with causal explanation. These models allow us to study both the environmental limitations and the deterministic consequences of political decision-making. Moreover, they provide parameters with which to measure historically varying structural forms of political activity.

This paper has only briefly illustrated several ways of combining increasingly available political data collections, partly inductive causal inference techniques, and deductive, testable theories derived from a rich tradition of qualitative political analysis.[34] Even though they have not explicitly introduced the time dimension, our test cases have implied several quite distinctive possibilities about the ongoing nature of the political process. The "competitive coexistence" model, as applied only to non-communist states, contained reequilibrating tendencies, which could also be labelled "negative feedback." The "communism vs. democracy" theory, on the other hand, was modelled as a case of disequilibrium, destabilizing change accomplished by positive feedback relationships. The hierarchical model of political development stood somewhere between these two reciprocal systems as a case of unidirectional change (assuming its coefficients remain positive) without

---

[34] That the inductive and deductive interaction of concepts and data using these methods can go beyond merely obvious relationships is indicated by the differences between the magnitudes of the simple correlations in Table 1 and the causal links in Table 3. Straight forward factor analysis of Table 1 would not have discovered the causal configuration of Figure 2.

There are a number of inductive data analysis procedures, however, which are beginning to suggest possible causal inferences. If simple additive causal theories are appropriate for example, factor analysis may detect them. If, on the other hand, developmental sequences exist like those in Figure 1.A, one should apply other techniques. Robert Abelson has informally suggested comparing structural similarities between Guttman's theory of the simplex and the equivalent pyramidal structure of recursive causal systems. At least for simple learning problems, simple developmental sequences and nearly perfect simplices seem to exist that are causally interpretable. See 25, 26, 27, 31.

major feedback relationships. Undoubtedly the world of politics—of power, influence, and authority relationships—includes all of these possibilities.

Perhaps the strongest arguments in favor of causal models like those we have discussed is that they help answer the central "who gets what, when, and why" questions of political analysis. Leaving more or less implicit many of the persuasion or reasoning processes accounting for the magnitudes of certain dependence coefficients, causal models can nonetheless help explain what maintains or changes the distribution of political power, social respect, and mental and physical health within particular societies. Internationally, for example, the tentative analyses of the present paper have suggested that most European nations have high political participation levels because of their high levels of urbanization, literacy, and media development. The citizenry of countries with little urbanization, many illiterates, and few mass media are less fortunate in this respect. Free political institutions in the Western world are in part maintained by their tendency to decrease violent domestic behavior which itself finds expression within more radical voting positions that are tolerated only by open societies.

## BIBLIOGRAPHY

This bibliography is intended to be suggestive rather than exhaustive of recent literature on the causal inference problem.

1. ALKER, H. R., JR. "Regionalism versus Universalism in Comparing Nations," in B. RUSSETT, H. ALKER, K. DEUTSCH, H. LASSWELL, World Handbook of Political and Social Indicators. New Haven: Yale University Press, 1964.
2. ———. Mathematics and Politics. New York: Macmillan Co., 1965.
3. ——— and HOPKINS, R. "Aggregate Data on Political Development: An Appraisal." In preparation.
4. ALLARDT, E. "Implications of Intra-Country Variations and Regional Imbalances for Cross-National Research," in R. MERRITT and S. ROKKAN, Comparing Nations. New Haven: Yale University Press, 1966.
5. ANDO, A., FISHER, F. M., and SIMON, H. A. Essays on the Structure of Social Science Models. Cambridge: M.I.T. Press, 1963.
6. BLALOCK, H. M., JR. "Evaluating the Relative Importance of Variables," American Sociological Review, XXVI (1961), 866-74.
7. ———. Causal Inferences in Nonexperimental Research. Chapel Hill: University of North Carolina Press, 1964.
8. ———. "Theory Building and the Statistical Concept of Interaction," American Sociological Review, XXX (June, 1965), 374-80.
9. BOUDON, R. "Methodes d'analyse causale," Revue Française de Sociologie, VI (January-March, 1965), 24-43.
10. ———. "A Method of Linear Causal Analysis: Dependence Analysis," American Sociological Review, XXX (June, 1965), 365-74.
11. CAMPBELL, A., CONVERSE, P., MILLER, W. and STOKES, D. The American Voter. New York: Wiley, 1960.
12. CAMPBELL, D. T., and STANLEY, J. S. "Experimental and Quasi-Experimental Designs for Research on Teaching," in N. L. GAGE (ed.), Handbook of Research on Teaching. Chicago: Rand McNally, 1963. Pp. 171-246.

13. CAMPBELL, D. T. "From Description to Experimentation: Interpreting Trends as Quasi-Experiments," in C. HARRIS (ed.), *Problems in Measuring Change*. Madison: University of Wisconsin Press, 1963. Pp. 212-42.
14. COLEMAN, J. *An Introduction to Mathematical Sociology*. New York: Macmillan Co., 1964.
15. ———. "The Mathematical Study of Change." Mimeographed, 1965.
16. DAHL, R. A. "The Power Analysis Approach to the Study of Politics," to appear in the *International Encyclopedia of the Social Sciences*. Macmillan Co., forthcoming.
17. DECHART, C. R. "Mutual Causal Processes in Political and International Systems." *American Behavioral Scientist*, Vol. IX, No. 7 (March, 1966), pp. 8-14.
18. DEUTSCH, K. W., "Autonomy and Boundaries According to Communication Theory," in R. R. GRINKER (ed.), *Toward a Unified Theory of Human Behavior*. New York: Basic Books, 1956. Pp. 278-97.
19. ———. *The Nerves of Government*. New York: Macmillan Co., 1963.
20. FATOUROS, A. A. "Sartre on Colonialism," *World Politics*, XVII (July, 1965), 703-19.
21. FEIGL, H. "Notes on Causality," in H. FEIGL and M. BRODBECK (eds.), *Readings in the Philosophy of Science*. New York: Appleton-Century-Crofts, 1963. Pp. 408-18.
22. FRISCH, R. *Statistical Confluence Analysis by Means of Complete Regression Systems*. Oslo: University Institute of Economics, 1934.
23. GRUNBAUM, A. "Causality and the Science of Human Behavior," in H. FEIGL and M. BRODBECK (eds.), *Readings in the Philosophy of Science*. New York: Appleton-Century-Crofts, 1953. Pp. 766-78.
24. GUTTMAN, L. "A New Approach to Factor Analysis: the Radex," in P. F. LAZARSFELD (ed.), *Mathematical Thinking in the Social Sciences*. Glencoe: Free Press, 1955. Pp. 258-348.
25. ———. "Order Analysis of Correlation Matrices," in R. B. CATTELL (ed.), *Handbook of Multivariate Experimental Psychology*. Chicago: Rand McNally. In press.
26. ———. "A General Nonmetric Technique for Finding the Smallest Euclidean Space for a Configuration of Points," *Psychometrika*, 1966, forthcoming.
27. ———. "The Structure of Interrelations among Intelligence Tests," in *Proceedings of the Invitational Conference on Testing Problems* of the Educational Testing Service, held in New York, October 31, 1964.
28. HANSON, N. R. "Causal Chains," *Mind*, LXIV (July, 1955), 289-311.
29. HOOD, W. C., and KOOPMANS, T. C. (eds.). *Studies in Econometric Method*. New York: Wiley & Sons, 1953.
30. HUNTINGTON, S. "Political Development and Political Decay," *World Politics*, XVII (April, 1965), 386-430.
31. KAISER, H. F. "Scaling a Simplex," *Psychometrika*, XXVII (June, 1962), 155-62.
32. KAPLAN, A. *The Conduct of Inquiry*. San Francisco: Chandler, 1964.
33. KENDALL, M. G., and STUART, A. *The Advanced Theory of Statistics*. London: Griffen & Co., 1961.
34. KOOPMANS, T. C. (ed.). *Statistical Inference in Dynamic Economic Models*. New York: Wiley & Sons, 1950.
35. LAZARSFELD, P. "Evidence and Inference in Social Research," *Daedalus*, LXXXVII (Fall, 1958), 99-130.
36. ———. "The Algebra of Dichotomous Systems," in H. SOLOMON (ed.), *Item Analysis and Prediction*. Stanford: Stanford University Press, 1959.
37. LERNER, D. *The Passing of Traditional Society*. Glencoe: Free Press, 1958.
38. ———. "Toward a Communication Theory of Modernization," in L. W. PYE (ed.), *Communications and Political Development*. Princeton: Princeton University Press, 1963. Pp. 327-50.
39. MACINTYRE, A. "A Mistake about Causality in Social Science," in P. LASLETT and W. A. RUNCIMAN (eds.), *Philosophy, Politics and Society*. New York: Barnes and Noble, 1962. Pp. 48-70.
40. MACIVER, R. M. *Social Causation*. Boston: Ginn & Co., 1942.
41. MARUYAMA, M. "The Second Cybernetics: Deviation-Amplifying Mutual Causal Processes," in *General Systems: Yearbook of the Society for General Systems Research*, VIII (1963), 233-41.

42. MILLER, W., and STOKES, D. "Constituency Influence in Congress," *American Political Science Review*, LVII (March, 1963), 45-56.
43. MYRDAL, G. *Economic Theory and Underdeveloped Regions.* London, G. Duckworth, 1957.
44. NAGEL, F. *The Structure of Science.* New York: Harcourt, Brace & World, 1961.
45. SIMON, H. A. *Models of Man.* New York: Wiley, 1957.
46. SOROKIN, P. A. Sociocultural Causality, Space, Time. Durham: Duke University Press, 1943.
47. TINBERGEN, J. *Statistical Testing of Business Cycle Theories, II.* Geneva: League of Nations, 1937.
48. TINTNER, G. *Econometrics.* New York: Wiley, 1952.
49. TUKEY, J. W. "Causation, Regression and Path Analysis," in O. KEMPTHORNE *et al.* (eds.), *Statistics and Mathematics in Biology.* Ames: Iowa State College Press, 1954. Pp. 35-66.
50. VALAVANIS, S. *Econometrics.* New York: McGraw-Hill, 1959.
51. WOLD, H., in association with JUREEN, L. *Demand Analysis.* New York: Wiley, 1953.
52. WOLD, H. "Ends and Means in Econometric Model Building," in U. GRENANDER (ed.), *Probability and Statistics: The Harold Cramer Volume.* Stockholm: Almquist & Wiksell, 1959. Pp. 355-434.
53. WRIGHT, S. "The Method of Path Coefficients," *Annals of Mathematical Statistics,* V (September, 1934), 161-215.
54. ———. "The Interpretation of Multivariate Systems," in O. KEMPTHORNE *et al.,* *Statistics and Mathematics in Biology.* Ames: Iowa State College Press, 1954. Pp. 11-33.
55. ———. "The Treatment of Reciprocal Interaction, with or without Lag, in Path Analysis," *Biometrics,* XVI (September, 1960), 423-45.

# The Representational Model in Cross-National Content Analysis

RICHARD L. MERRITT[1]

*Yale University*

Systematic content analysis as a tool for political research is not particularly new. In primitive form it flourished during the 1930's. Students of journalism and others ascertained attention patterns, as indicated by column inches or occasionally by word counts, for wide varieties of newspapers and other publications; they compared patterns of attention to political events in the same publications over time; they contrasted political interest in large metropolitan dailies to that in small-town weeklies; they spent much time with questions of appropriate sampling and validation techniques.

It remained for Harold D. Lasswell and his colleagues, however, to develop content analysis as a tool specifically for comparative political research. Their studies of attention patterns in the "prestige papers" of five countries set standards of precision, clarity, and objectivity that students of comparative political behavior have sought to emulate for well over a decade. Since then David C. McClelland, Karin Dovring, Robert C. North, Robert C. Angell, J. Zvi Namenwirth, Richard L. Merritt and Ellen B. Pirro, and others have undertaken substantial content analyses of aspects of the communication process relevant for the cross-national study of politics.

The increasing importance of content analysis as a research tool, no less than the fact that increasingly large sums are being spent for studies using the technique, suggests that the time has come to pause and re-examine some of its fundamental assumptions. One important assumption concerns the nature of the "representational model" used in such studies, that is, the posited relationship between observed and unobserved aspects of the communication process. In this paper I shall express my own concern about developments along this line, paying particular attention to some of the cross-national content analyses of recent years. One caveat at the outset: If my comments appear unduly pessimistic, it

[1] Research on this project has been supported by the Yale Political Data Program.

is because of the cavalier treatment given to this problem by some scholars rather than because of the fact that the problem itself is irresolvable. The problem can be resolved. But, as I shall suggest, its resolution will require both serious thinking about the methodology of content analysis and serious experimental work.

### Content Analysis and the Communication Process

The communication process, in Lasswell's phrase (slightly modified), deals with WHY WHO says WHAT to WHOM and with WHAT EFFECT—expressed schematically in Figure 1. Content analysis focuses on the message, or the WHAT in Lasswell's

FIGURE 1

## THE COMMUNICATION PROCESS

| Motivation WHY | | Communicator WHO | | Encoding | | Message WHAT | | Decoding | | Recipient WHOM | | Effect WHAT EFFECT |
|---|---|---|---|---|---|---|---|---|---|---|---|---|

formulation. It is the systematic, objective, and quantitative characterization of content variables manifest or latent in a message.[2] In principle any type of message may be content analyzed: interesting cross-national work has been performed on movies by Martha Wolfenstein and Nathan Leites;[3] on plays by Donald V. McGranahan;[4] and on doodling and designs on vases by Elliot Aronson.[5] To date, however, most cross-national content analyses have dealt with written messages; and it is with these that this chapter will be primarily concerned.

Content analysis research entails a number of distinct but interrelated steps. This is not the place to discuss its methodology at great length; but a brief outline of these steps, and some of the problems encountered at each, will help to set the stage for some remarks on the representational model.

---

[2] Bernard Berelson, *Content Analysis in Communication Research* (Glencoe: Free Press, 1952), p. 18. This paper will not deal with the nonfrequency type of content analysis discussed by Alexander L. George, "Quantitative and Qualitative Approaches to Content Analysis," in Ithiel de Sola Pool (ed.), *Trends in Content Analysis* (Urbana: University of Illinois Press, 1959), pp. 7-32.

[3] Martha Wolfenstein and Nathan Leites, *Movies: A Psychological Study* (Glencoe: Free Press, 1950).

[4] Donald V. McGranahan and Ivor Wayne, "German and American Traits Reflected in Popular Drama," *Human Relations*, I (1948), 429-55.

[5] Elliot Aronson, "The Need for Achievement as Measured by Graphic Expression," in John W. Atkinson (ed.), *Motives in Fantasy, Action, and Society: A Method of Assessment and Study* (Princeton: Van Nostrand, 1958), pp. 249-65.

*The Formulation of Hypotheses.* Ideally, the analyst formulates his hypotheses (as well as their alternatives) for testing at the outset of his project. Content analysis is useful only when the researcher has questions of a quantitative nature—how often? how much? how many? with what covariance?—that can be answered by counting the appearance of a limited number of content variables in a given body of data. It is not particularly helpful if the task of research is merely to determine the timing of a sequence of events (such as the death of Stalin and the subsequent emergence of Khrushchev as the Soviet leader); it is of more use in trying to determine what effects the events had upon people's perceptions, attitudes, and values (such as in messages communicated by the Soviet elite). The task of the analyst is to frame his questions so that quantitative data can answer them clearly, directly, and simply.

It must be added that there is usually considerable interplay between the hypothesis-formulation stage and data-gathering stages in a content analysis, as in other types of research. It may even turn out that the most fruitful hypotheses do not emerge clearly until after the analyst has examined his preliminary findings. Other important scientific discoveries have resulted from studies based on hunches rather than rigidly formulated propositions. Sometimes research of this sort is inefficient; but the analyst who is sensitive to his findings may produce more interesting and meaningful results than the analyst who is blindly testing preformulated hypotheses.

*The Selection of an Appropriate Sample.* The determination of what body of material could be used to test the hypotheses rests upon both the availability of data and the nature of the inferences to be drawn from the analysis. To get an idea of values current among Soviet elites, for instance, it would be ideal if we had access to the minutes of Presidium meetings. But such data are not at our disposal. In their absence, will the news columns of *Pravda* or *Izvestia* give us the information we want? Similarly, if our files of the most nearly ideal body of material are incomplete, it may be necessary to work out a compromise: accepting the information loss due to missing data; estimating the nature of the missing data through statistical techniques already developed; selecting a second-best source of data; possibly even using available files of the first choice as a check on trends present in the second choice.

The sampling procedure itself is a function of the type and amount of information needed to test the hypotheses as well as of what economists call the "opportunity cost" of securing a certain amount of information. Appropriate sampling techniques include random sampling, using a table of random digits; systematic sampling, selecting every nth item in a series, or picking newspaper issues on the 1st and 15th of every month; and stratified random sampling for bodies of material that can be broken down into discrete categories.

Validating the sample, to see whether or not it is actually representative of the universe of items from which it was drawn, can be problematical. For random samples, standard statistical techniques (e.g., "split-halves" technique within the sample itself, or comparison of the sample with an independent sample from the same universe of items) are readily available. Often in political research, however, we cannot be quite certain of the randomness of the sample. Published foreign office documents, for instance, are clearly not exhaustive of all documents in a country's foreign office. Compilers of such documents necessarily use some criteria of relevance in deciding which items to include and which to exclude. The extent to which a random sample of the published collection actually approximates the distribution of documents in the entire files is a question that demands an answer if we are to credit any content analysis of the sample. Statistical techniques will tell us whether or not the sample is representative of the published documents, but correction factors are necessary to answer the more difficult question. Or else, some serious digging must be done in the particular country's foreign office files.

*The Selection of Units of Analysis.* Content analysts have generally used three types of analytical units: space, symbols, and themes. Determining the relative amount of space devoted in a message to a particular topic is often a good indicator of the communicator's concern with the topic. If we view words as symbols for content analysis purposes, then establishing a list of relevant symbols is a crucial step. The experience of the RADIR project—which concentrated on "symbols supposed to reflect trends in world politics with particular reference to changing attitudes toward the values of democracy, fraternity, security, and well-being"—is instructive in this regard. Pool writes:

Our own procedure in attempting to draw up a relatively valid list was to draw upon the best knowledge available and to use a long enough list so that the arbitrary decisions about inclusion or exclusion would affect the relatively infrequent terms in the tails of the word usage distribution, rather than more common words. To draw up the list we called upon Harold D. Lasswell, for thirty years one of the leading students of political movements and propaganda. The list he drew up consisted of nouns, although the listed words were also counted when they appeared in other forms. The list was then subjected to the test of use. Any expert, by pure oversight, might omit some symbols of obvious importance. Our readers were, therefore, instructed to note and report any additional symbols that seemed appropriate to the list.[6]

Some of the more recent cross-national content analyses have dealt with themes. Angell delineated 40 value dimensions relevant for Soviet and American ideology (e.g., "Mode of Ownership of Property"), and coded "elite" publications in the two countries according to several possible positions along each dimension. McClelland searched children's readers in 41 countries for their concern with a need for achievement, affiliation, and power. And Stone's General Inquirer "tags" words (which can also be used as symbols) according to a predetermined list of concepts. Which type of content variable is most appropriate for a particular analysis rests, of course, upon the type of information needed to test the researcher's hypotheses.

*Establishing Procedures for Counting.* Perhaps the simplest type of content analysis uses a frequency count of the appearance of the content variables. Merritt, in his examination of the colonial American press, for instance, tabulated the frequency which which place-name symbols occurred.[7] Angell counted the frequency with which Soviet and American publications took positions along his 40 value variables. In the former case, each reference to a unit of analysis was recorded; in the latter, no content variable could be coded more than once in any single communication.

It is also possible to add vectors to frequency counts. The RADIR studies noted whether the context of the tabulated symbols was positive, neutral, or negative. The Stanford project on conflict and integration, directed by North, codes communications along several dimensions, such as "good-bad," "active-passive,"

---

[6] Ithiel de Sola Pool, with Harold D. Lasswell, Daniel Lerner, *et al., The "Prestige Papers": A Survey of Their Editorials* (Stanford: Stanford University Press, 1952), pp. 16-17.

[7] Richard L. Merritt, *Symbols of American Community, 1735-1775* (New Haven: Yale University Press, 1966).

"strong-weak," and "hostility-friendship."[8] The Yale Arms Control Project coded French, German, British, and American editorial responses to arms control proposals along 5-point or 7-point scales according to the perceived specificity or diffuseness of the proposal, its operationality or nonoperationality, the level of affect displayed, and so forth.[9]

In either event objectivity requires that these technical aspects of the content analysis be specified in advance, and that throughout the analysis there be strict adherence to the coding procedure.

A special problem that arises with computerized content analysis is the transformation of existing material into texts that can be handled by current programming techniques. In the case of the General Inquirer, this requires a certain amount of editing: breaking "complex sentences down into simple thought-sequence units";[10] adding information not normally found in the computer's memory drum (e.g., adding parenthetically "warm vacation place" to references to Florida); clarifying the referent of ambiguous words (references to the singer George London and the city of London), and "tagging" some words or combinations of words relevant to concepts in which the analyst is interested (e.g., "affect," "European economic integration"). The Stanford project utilizes "evaluative assertion analysis" which translates messages into a "simple, three-element assertive format."[11] Such transforma-

---

[8] *Cf.* the special issue on "Case Studies in Conflict," edited by Robert C. North, *Journal of Conflict Resolution*, VI (1962), 197-268; and Robert C. North, Ole R. Holsti, M. George Zaninovich, and Dina A. Zinnes, *Content Analysis: A Handbook with Applications for the Study of International Crisis* (Evanston: Northwestern University Press, 1963). This paper does not deal with the representational model used by the Stanford project, primarily because I have found nowhere a detailed discussion of sampling techniques; *cf.* J. David Singer, "Data-Making in International Relations," *Behavioral Science*, X (1965), 68-80, especially p. 71.

[9] For a preliminary analysis, see Richard L. Merritt and Ellen B. Pirro, *Press Attitudes to Arms Control in Four Countries, 1946-1963* (New Haven: Yale University, Political Science Research Library, mimeographed, 1966).

[10] Philip J. Stone, Robert F. Bales, J. Zvi Namenwirth, and Daniel M. Ogilvie, "The General Inquirer: A Computer System for Content Analysis and Retrieval Based on the Sentence as a Unit of Information," *Behavioral Science*, VII (1962), 492.

[11] North *et al.*, *Content Analysis*, p. 91. The difficulty of working with evaluative assertion analysis may be illustrated by the example of its operation given on p. 93. The main author of the chapter in question, Holsti, turns the following sentence from a Communist Chinese newspaper,

*The treacherous American aggressors are abetting the corrupt ruling circles of Japan.*
into four evaluative assertions:

1. Americans are treacherous.
2. Americans are aggressors.
3. Americans are abetting Japanese ruling circles.
4. Japanese ruling circles are corrupt.

If we follow the normal canons of logic, the four assertions are most assuredly *not* a reasonable restatement of the original sentence.

tions, although seemingly simple, may contribute significantly to the level of error in any content analysis.

*Training Coders and Testing Coder Reliability.* There is general agreement that coders need to be sufficiently trained and have enough understanding of the coding categories that two coders working independently will produce quite similar results. This implies a necessity for working out coding manuals and other training procedures. When coding is being performed for the analyst who originated the coding procedures, there is a marked tendency to postpone any effort to formalize the techniques, that is, to write them down in detail. If students and scholars at other universities are to be able to use the procedures, however, explicit and precise coding manuals are imperative. With time, as computerized content analysis becomes more fully developed, it will be possible simply to exchange data preparation routines and computer programs that can be used anywhere by a novice in "cookbook" fashion.

Testing intercoder reliability is a relatively underdeveloped facet of content analysis. This is not to say that techniques to measure reliability have not been developed. Or even that Berelson's complaint of a decade and a half ago is still valid: "Whatever the actual state of reliability in content analysis, the published record is less than satisfactory. Only about 15-20% of the studies report the reliability of the analysis contained in them."[12] In fact, the most important cross-national analyses of recent years have been quite careful to discuss their problems of reliability.

Two key aspects of intercoder reliability checks have nonetheless received insufficient attention. The first is the question of acceptable levels of reliability. What does it mean when a content analyst reports that his reliability score for two coders, using a simple percentage agreement test,[13] is .70? How much more useful or valid is the analysis if the percentage agreement is .80 or .90? How does a reliability coefficient for the percentage agreement test compare with Scott's reliability index or with a Pearsonian product-moment correlation coefficient? Second, very little experimental information exists on the determinants of coder reliability. What role does the explicitness of the instructions in

[12] Berelson, *Content Analysis in Communication Research*, p. 172.

[13] For an excellent discussion of reliability indices, see William A. Scott, "Reliability of Content Analysis: The Case of Nominal Scale Coding," *Public Opinion Quarterly*, XIX (1955), 321-25.

the coding manual play? What type of training and practice procedures are most likely to enhance coder reliability? Does the difficulty of securing high intercoder reliability coefficients increase if themes rather than symbols are coded? What impact does the educational and intelligence level of the coder have upon his performance? It seems to me that attention to these basic issues would be fruitful for the future development of content analysis.[14]

## Inferences from Content Analysis

As suggested earlier, content analysis focuses on the message—or the WHAT in Lasswell's formulation. Our reasons for wanting to know the substance or form of the message may be various. On the most trivial level, the message may merely be of intrinsic interest to us: we may be curious to know, for instance, what the Western European press says about a particular arms control proposal, or the frequency of certain types of word usage in the editorials of "elite" newspapers. More frequently, however, we are interested in the message because we think it contains clues about other, less directly observable, aspects of the communication process.[15]

Sometimes the content analyst is interested in the recipients of a set of messages—the WHOM of the earlier formula. Part of the justification for using "prestige papers" to estimate the mood of elites is, according to Pool, that these newspapers are "read by the elite."[16] The question of readership posed by Pool's assertion may be looked at in two ways. On the one hand, we would like to know who the actual, as opposed to the intended, recipients of the message are. Who in fact reads the *New York Times?* Of those, who reads the editorials? What percentage of the reader's total time spent per day in gaining new information is devoted to perusal of the *Times?* On the other hand, what do the intended

[14] What is proposed is methodological research similar to that on interviewer bias performed by early researchers. For a graphic description of the process of training coders, see Charles P. Smith and Sheila Feld, "How to Learn the Method of Content Analysis for *n* Achievement, *n* Affiliation, and *n* Power," in Atkinson (ed.), *Motives in Fantasy, Action, and Society,* pp. 685-818; and Feld and Smith, "An Evaluation of the Objectivity of the Method of Content Analysis," in *ibid.,* pp. 234-41.

[15] A number of important points cannot be discussed in this paper. One is the problem of error stemming from the encoding and decoding aspects of the communication process. A second is the question of inferences drawn on the *latent and manifest levels* of communication. Third, there is the issue of whether the message performs an *instrumental or representational function* for the communicator. On this last point, see Pool (ed.), *Trends in Content Analysis,* pp. 206-12.

[16] Pool *et al., The "Prestige Papers,"* p. 7.

recipients of the messages in fact read? What percentage of them
reads the message? Which of them also read other (and possibly
contradictory) messages as well? As will be suggested later, the
answers to such questions lie not in a content analysis itself, nor
even in the force of logic. Questions of actual as opposed to
intended readership lie more properly with various types of media
analysis through survey research.

The issue of WHAT EFFECT the message has upon its recipient is still thornier. Pool's assertion that the "prestige" newspapers
are not only read by elites but also "influence them" raises un-
answered questions about individual and group decision-making
processes.[17] To be sure, it is important to know what is made
available to a decision-making system. But it is even more important to know what is assimilated or accepted for use by the
system. For instance, suppose that a person reads a message
telling him to vote for a particular candidate in an election, and
then goes out to vote for him. Can we infer a causal relationship
between the message and the ballot? It may be that the person
happened to pick up the message as he was already on his way to
vote for the candidate. Or it may be that persons likely to vote for
the candidate are more likely than others to happen upon such
literature. Or it may be that the message did indeed persuade the
voter to opt for the candidate. At this stage in political research,
determining the effect of communication upon attitude change is
simply not a function of content analysis itself (unless the analyst
has independent validating evidence, such as that produced by
experimental psychology, in which case the content analysis may
be superfluous).

Sometimes we are interested in determining WHO the communicator is. This is the case in propaganda analysis where we
assume that, if we know the source of a message, we shall also
know the extent to which it is likely to contain biased information.
Lasswell and his colleagues used content analysis techniques
during World War II with great effectiveness to determine the
extent to which certain American publications contained news and
editorial comment stemming from Nazi sources.[18] Discovering who
the author of a message is has also been important in some types

[17] *Ibid.*

[18] Harold D. Lasswell, "Detection: Propaganda Detection and the Courts," in
Harold D. Lasswell, Nathan Leites, and Associates, *The Language of Politics: Studies
in Quantitative Semantics* (New York: Stewart, 1949), pp. 173-232.

of literary detective work. Recent efforts by Mosteller and Wallace, using electronic computers, to infer who wrote which of the *Federalist* papers are exemplary in this regard.[19]

In cross-national political research it is usually clear who the communicator is. Sleuthing is generally directed to other ends. The question of who the communicator is nonetheless raises in elementary form the basic issue of the representational model used in content analysis research. That is, are we interested in the communicator himself, because of his personal attributes? Or do we examine his messages because he seems to be speaking for some other group, such as the organization or culture of which he is a member? Another way of looking at these questions is to ask what motivates the communicator: WHY does he transmit a particular message?

### The Representational Model:
### Why the Communicator Communicates

Individual motivation rests upon a variety of subtly operating factors in the human psyche. Not the least of these is the nature of the *information* that an individual has at his disposal when he makes decisions. The amount of information available to the individual is limited by both chance and choice. He does not see, for instance, most newspapers published in the United States, nor is it likely that he could manage to read them were they all delivered on his doorstep. Every individual consciously and unconsciously screens out certain types of information: he may deliberately choose to skip some sections of his morning newspaper, such as the women's page or the financial section; if he reads the paper when he is tired he may miss some of the more subtle points expressed by editorial writers; moreover, experimental evidence indicates that some people literally do not see certain items that disagree with their preconceptions. In contrast to the input of current information—values, attitudes, beliefs—there is also information stored in *memory*. In the individual's active memory is much information that can be readily recalled, information ranging from the date of his birth to his perception of the course of events in Vietnam. More deeply stored information includes items of very low salience, such as the telephone number of his childhood residence, as well as such repressed data as painful emotional ex-

---

[19] Frederick Mosteller and David L. Wallace, *Inference and Disputed Authorship: The Federalist* (Reading, Mass., Palo Alto, Calif., and London: Addison Wesley, 1964).

periences in childhood. Individual motivation also rests upon a person's *perception of alternative courses of action* as well as their likely outcomes. Some behavior is purposeful: a person postulates a set of goals and then implements them as best he can. At the same time it must be added that random or habitual behavior often plays a role in the communication process, in determining what things a person will communicate and how he will communicate them.

In short, individual motivation is at best a complex mix of both current and stored information, perceptions of modes of behavior, and some nonrational factors such as chance and habit. If the task of content analysis is to infer a person's motivations from his messages, then what is needed is a sound theory bridging the gaps among motivation, verbal behavior, and other forms of behavior. Freudian psychology presents one possible bridge: the goal of the psychoanalyst (who was instrumental, by the way, in the development of content analysis techniques) is to try to account for individual behavior through the examination of a wide range of the individual's messages. Some scholars have even tried to "psychoanalyze" historical personages by content analyzing their verbal messages and comparing these messages with those produced by currently living personality types, whose characteristics have been analyzed clinically.[20]

The problem of motivation becomes still more complex as soon as we move from the personal to the public realm. Political psychology aside, content analysis generally deals not with the private utterances of a man lying on a psychoanalyst's couch but with his public messages—the speeches he delivers, the pictures he paints, the memoranda and position papers he drafts, the editorials he writes, and so forth. If we are looking for the reason—or motivation—for such communications, then we may examine either the man's personality structure, or his relationship with the environment, or both. The question to be asked is, *Whom or what does the individual represent when he communicates?*

One possible answer is that he represents himself and no one else. He is seeking to express his own mind rather than pretending to be the spokesman for any group or culture. Such an answer, however, poses new questions: (1) How accurately does the

---

[20] For an excellent example, see Alexander L. and Juliette L. George, *Woodrow Wilson and Colonel House: A Personality Study* (New York: Day, 1956).

message reflect his "true" feelings? (2) Why did he choose the particular mode of communication that he did? (3) Why did others permit the article to be published or the speech to be delivered publicly? To what extent were they in agreement with the values, attitudes, and beliefs expressed in the message? If the level of agreement were high, then we might argue that the communicator, regardless of his intentions and preferences, may be perceived to be "representing" someone else (e.g., those in control of the means of communication). (4) What influence did the communicator's group memberships have on the substance and form of his message? To what extent was the communicator aware of such group influences? Did he seek to counteract them? Again, regardless of intention or preference, the extent to which the message reflects the actual constellation of group values, attitudes, and beliefs may be taken as an indication of the extent to which the communicator represents the group. The task, however, is to discover the degree of congruence.

An alternative answer is that the communicator is in fact representative of some other group. Thus we may be less interested in the remarks of a specific general as an indicator of his personal views than as an indicator of what "generals" or even the "military elite" think. Among the significant questions that arise if we take this position are the following: (1) How accurately does the communicator's message reflect the "true" feelings of the group? (2) To what extent is the linkage perceived or consciously sought by either the individual or the "represented" group? In the previous paragraph I suggested that a representational model might be inferred in certain circumstances despite specific disclaimers on the part of the communicator that he does or is seeking to speak for the particular group. The other side of this is the extent to which a communicator may be said to speak for a group even though the group disavows him and openly rejects his views. (3) In the presence of a clear link between communicator and group, how can we tell whether the communicator is consciously trying to mirror group attitudes or whether he is writing to persuade the group to adopt new attitudes? In the latter case the manifest content of the message might deviate substantially from group norms. (4) Given the fact that most people are members of more than one group, what is the mix of different group influences that is relevant for any single individual's messages? When a doctor, who happens also to be a Catholic and of Italian extraction, writes an editorial in the *Journal of the American Medical Association,* how sure can we be that his views "represent" those of the rest of the medical profession, which comprises by and large Protestants of Anglo-Saxon origin? (5) To what extent is *any* message that a person communicates influenced by the overall culture of which he is a member? That is, how much by way of group or cultural values creeps autonomously into every message?

If the purpose of content analysis, then, is to extrapolate from observed variables in messages to nonobserved motivational variables, two interrelated questions are crucial. First, is the communicator perceived or assumed to be representing his own views, those of the group or groups to which he belongs, or those of his overall culture? And, second, what mix of conscious and unconscious elements goes into the formulation of his message? Let us turn to some of the more recent cross-national content analyses to see how such questions have been treated.

*Pool et al.: The "Prestige Papers."* Perhaps the most elaborate of these studies is the Hoover Institute's research project on Revolution and the Development of International Relations (RADIR Project). The published portions of the project analyze symbols of democracy and internationalism in newspapers from five countries, covering the years from 1890 to 1949:

| | |
|---|---|
| Great Britain | *The Times* (1890-1949) |
| Russia | *Novoe Vremia* (1892-1917); *Izvestia* (1918-1949) |
| United States | *The New York Times* (1900-1949) |
| France | *Le Temps* (1900-1942); *Le Monde* (1945-1949) |
| Germany | *Norddeutsche allgemeine Zeitung* (1910-1920); *Frankfurter Zeitung* (1920-1932); *Völkischer Beobachter* (1933-1945) |

As justification for the decision to examine editorials in these newspapers, Pool writes:

> In each major power one newspaper stands out as an organ of elite opinion. Usually semiofficial, always intimate with the government, these "prestige papers" are read by public officials, journalists, scholars, and business leaders. They seldom have large circulations, yet they have enormous influence. They are read not only in their own countries, but also abroad by those whose business it is to keep track of world affairs. They differ among themselves, but, despite national and temporal differences, they are a distinct species. It is generally possible to name with fair

confidence one paper in any given country which plays the role of prestige paper at any given time.

The prestige paper is in some respects a good index of elite behavior. It is read by the elite and influences them. In addition, it is produced by men who have themselves become part of the elite and share the typical life pattern of the elite.[21]

The argument is plausible, but is it true? We know that the "prestige papers" are representative of something or someone. But of what or of whom? To take a recent example, *New York Times* editorials on the issue of American participation in the Vietnam struggle, prior to the summer of 1965 at least, could scarcely be called indicative of government policy or even of informed opinion among American elite groupings. It is doubtless true that—over the long run, and given a wide range of issues—the *New York Times* is closer to "official" or "elite" opinion than any other single publication in the United States. Despite the fairness of this assumption, it cannot be a fully satisfactory answer to the question raised above until empirical tests can show an actual (as opposed to an imputed) relationship between the distribution of attitudes in *New York Times* editorials and policies pursued or attitudes held in official or elite quarters.

A second set of questions was raised earlier: Does the elite in fact read the prestige papers, either in the United States or elsewhere? And how can we verify whether or not the editorials influence those who read them? In these regards intensive interviews with samples of elite groupings might give us relevant answers.[22]

A third question is the extent to which the prestige papers compare in their expressed values, attitudes, and beliefs with the

---

[21] Pool, *et al.*, *The "Prestige Papers,"* pp. 1, 7. In this analysis I shall not deal separately with other studies using a similar representational model. Cf. Wilbur Schramm (ed.), *One Day in the World's Press: Fourteen Great Newspapers on a Day of Crisis, with Translations and Facsimile Reproductions* (Stanford: Stanford University Press, 1959); and J. Zvi Namenwirth and Thos. L. Brewer, "Elite Editorial Comment on the European and Atlantic Communities in Four Countries," in Philip J. Stone, Dexter C. Dunphy, Marshall Smith, and Daniel M. Ogilvie (eds.), *General Inquirer: A General Approach to Content Analysis* (Cambridge: M.I.T. Press, 1966).

[22] What I have in mind is a series of studies similar to those performed at the Survey Research Center of The University of Michigan on the interaction between congressmen and their constituents; cf. Warren E. Miller and Donald E. Stokes, "Constituency Influence in Congress," *American Political Science Review*, LVII (1963), 45-56. A beginning may be found in James N. Rosenau, *National Leadership and Foreign Policy: A Case Study in the Mobilization of Public Support* (Princeton: Princeton University Press, 1963).

other newspapers in their own countries. Two projects currently under way at Yale University are seeking clues to resolve this problem. One, under the direction of J. Zvi Namenwirth, is content analyzing three "elite" and three "mass" newspapers in the United States, using the General Inquirer procedure. The other is investigating editorial attitudes in a wide variety of French, West German, British, and American journals toward specific arms control events and proposals; a comparison of the prestige papers with the others will at least give us an idea of how typical they are of the press of the different countries.

Finally, the study of "elite" newspapers poses a problem similar to that faced by students of community power structures who concentrate upon "community influentials." A newspaper may enjoy a reputation for influence when in fact it is not influential. Other newspapers, although perhaps somewhat less "intellectual" than the prestige papers, may be widely read by elite groupings. Or it is possible that a newspaper loses whatever influence among the elite it once had. If we continue to concentrate upon attention and value patterns in newspapers after they have passed their zenith, we may be deluding ourselves about actual trends in the country. But, then, how do we know when the star of an elite journal is falling and that of another publication is taking its place?

*Karin Dovring: Land Reform as a Propaganda Theme.* The focus of this study is the ideological coloration of demands for land reform. Ten documents covering the period from 1891 to 1952 are analyzed:

| | |
|---|---|
| Vatican | Papal Encyclical, "De rerum novarum" (1891) |
| Soviet Union | Lenin, seven pamphlets and speeches (1913-1919) |
| Vatican | Papal Encyclical, "Quadragesimo Anno" (1931) |
| Vatican | Pope Pius XII, Pentecost message (1941) |
| France | Tanguy-Prigent (Socialist and later Minister of Agriculture), "Dèmocratie à la terre" (1945) |
| Hungary | András Sandór, "Land Reform in Hungary" (1947) |
| Bulgaria | Vulko Chervenkov (Secretary of the Central Committee of the Bulgarian Communist Party, later Prime Minister), speech, "Tasks of the Co-operative Farms" (1950) |

| Italy | Government statement on the need for land reform, "La Relazione Ministeriale" (1951) |
| Italy | Giuseppi Medici (Head of Ente Maremma, later Minister of Agriculture), "Il Contratto con i Contadini" (1952) |
| East Germany | West German Bundesministerium für gesamtdeutsche Fragen, pamphlet, "Auf dem Wege zur Kolchose" (1952) |

These documents are searched systematically for symbols of *identification,* of *demands* for certain values, and of *resistance* to other values. Dr. Dovring tabulates the frequency of the symbols, grouped into themes; determines their function (that is, whether they are symbols of identification, demand, or resistance); and notes whether their contexts are favorable or unfavorable.

As far as her representative model is concerned, Dr. Dovring writes that the ten documents have two things in common. First, "they are regarded as responsible statements justifying agrarian policy in practice in the respective countries after the Second World War." And, second, "they claim to deal with agrarian or social questions, but at the same time they are all living statements of current ideologies in conflict today."[23] Hence, the messages "represent" official opinion as well as official and unofficial ideologies.

Such a representational model poses a number of questions. First of all, the principle underlying the selection of particular documents is not stated anywhere. This is particularly noticeable with respect to Communist proposals. Of all postwar statements on land reform in Eastern Europe (such as those cited in other parts of the book of which this study forms one chapter), for example, why were those by Sandór and Chervenkov rather than others included in this survey? Granted that they are authoritative, are they also representative of land reform measures in Poland, Czechoslovakia, or Rumania? Similarly, is it true that the best statement of East German land reform measures and proposals is a pamphlet published by a West German government agency? Why not Wilhelm Pieck's speech in 1945 entitled "Junkerland in

[23] Karin Dovring, "Land Reform as a Propaganda Theme," in Folke Dovring, *Land and Labor in Europe, 1900-1950: A Comparative Survey of Recent Agrarian History* (The Hague: Martinus Nijhoff, 1956), p. 270.

Bauernhand!" or Walter Ulbricht's lengthy chapter on "The Democratic Land Reform"?[24]

Second, is there any measure of functional equivalence among
the different messages? That is, do they serve the same function
in all the societies included in the survey? Is it realistic to compare
a series of statements by Lenin during prerevolutionary and
revolutionary times with an Italian government statement on the
need for land reform? Since three of the ten documents stem from
the Vatican, it seems legitimate to question what role the Vatican
plays in European land reform. How much influence does it exert
over individual (noncommunist) governments? Or are the three
messages included to give an estimate of a changing mood in
European intellectual circles?

Third, it seems necessary to look closely at the function of a
particular message in its society. Put another way, why did the
communicator transmit the message? Was it merely to announce
a new policy generally acceptable to the population at large? Or
was it to persuade intransigent opponents of the need for such a
policy? Or was it an instrumental message designed to achieve
other ends (e.g., promising long-run support to land-hungry peasants in exchange for their support of other controversial measures)? Perhaps the clearest question arises here with respect to
Lenin's statements, four of which were pamphlets written in 1913
and directed to intellectuals, and the other three of which were
statements made to elements of the peasantry in the desperate
years of struggle, 1918-1919. It may turn out that several different
messages communicated by a single individual are more similar
(regardless of intent) than messages emanating from different
communicators; for studies of this sort we need some indication of
the magnitude of these differences.

*McClelland: The Achieving Society.* McClelland analyzed the
content of children's stories from 23 countries for the period 1920-
1929 (centering around 1925) and from 41 countries for the period
1946-1955 (centering around 1950), using the analytical framework developed for projective tests to measure the need for
achievement (*n* Achievement), for affiliation (*n* Affiliation), and

---

[24] Wilhelm Pieck, "Junkerland in Bauernhand!" speech on September 2, 1945,
in *Volkszeitung* (Dresden), September 6, 1945; Walter Ulbricht, "Die demokratische
Bodenreform," in *Zur Geschichte der neuesten Zeit* (Berlin: Dietz, 1955), Vol. I, part
1, pp. 208-38. The use of a West German source, by the way, puts Dr. Dovring in
the awkward position of having to invert all her findings on East Germany.

for power ( $n$ Power). Data on $n$ Achievement levels in these countries were then correlated with two indices of modern economic growth.

In the process of collecting the readers, four types of bias were introduced into the sample. With respect to the first three, the level of bias could be reduced significantly simply by gathering samples of stories from the countries now missing in McClelland's list. (1) At the outset, for reasons that are not made clear, McClelland decided to exclude from his sample countries lying in the tropics. This specification systematically eliminates all the Caribbean and Central American republics, most of the South American countries, most of Africa south of the Sahara, and all of Southeast Asia. (2) Communist Bloc countries are underrepresented: the sample includes only the Soviet Union, Poland, Hungary, and Bulgaria; it excludes, most likely due to the unavailability of data, Czechoslovakia, East Germany, Rumania, Yugoslavia, Albania, Communist China, North Vietnam, North Korea, and the Mongolian People's Republic. (The ratio of population in the former to the latter group of countries is approximately 1 to 3.) (3) There is a bias in favor of economically advanced countries. Perhaps this was unavoidable, since levels of education appear to be correlated with levels of economic growth. But, as it turns out, the average gross national product per capita in 1961 for the 41 countries (including Brazil, the analysis of whose readers was, according to McClelland, open to "coding bias") was $668, and for some 81 excluded countries $230, or about one third as much; the percentage growth in GNP per capita from about 1950 to 1960 was 3.41 per cent for 34 included countries for which we have data, as opposed to 2.54 per cent for 34 excluded countries for which data are available.[25] Since the focus of McClelland's study is the relationship between a societal need for achievement and that society's economic development, I cannot help but believe that this particular sampling bias severely limits the value of the findings, as well as the predictive value of his main hypothesis.

The fourth type of sampling bias cannot be rectified without scrapping all of McClelland's data and starting anew. This bias stems from the means used to collect the readers. After looking

[25] Data from Bruce M. Russett and Hayward R. Alker, Jr., Karl W. Deutsch, and Harold D. Lasswell, *World Handbook of Political and Social Indicators* (New Haven: Yale University Press, 1964), pp. 149-61.

unsuccessfully in the Library of Congress for such readers, Mc-
Clelland wrote to the ministries of education of the various countries, asking for three "widely-used" readers dating from 1925 and
1950. Where responses were not forthcoming, he relied upon book
dealers in the countries and upon private sources. Such a sampling
process may have been dictated by necessity, but we must be
absolutely clear about the fact that it could not produce (except
by the sheerest of accidents) a *random* sampling of readers used
in the countries during those time periods. We have no way of
knowing either how representative the selected readers are or how
"widely" they were used. And information of this sort is vital for
an evaluation of the project's findings.[26]

How appropriate are children's readers for an assessment of
societal values anyway? As will be seen, not even McClelland is
sure of the answer to this question. In fact, in the paragraphs that
follow I shall use his arguments and counter-arguments exten-
sively. The difference lies in the conclusions we reach.

McClelland first of all rejects the simple notion that the stories
in the readers "represent" solely characteristics of their author's
personalities. While recognizing that this may be true in part, he
sees the author not as a creator but as a mediator. The author
transmits aspects of the culture to a particular audience—"children
and the adults having to do with the education of children who
will decide whether their stories will be included in the textbooks
or not."[27] Such a position raises two problems. First, there are
several points in the process of transmitting values at which errors
of one sort or another can creep in. The author, for instance, has
a wide stock of folklore available to him when he sits down to
write. On what basis does he make his selection of stories to
retell? Can we safely conclude that his vision of cultural values
is reasonably accurate? His manner of writing may emphasize
some values in a story and relegate others to a minor role. What

---

[26] It is significant in this regard that McClelland himself reveals a tendency to
question the representativeness of the readers when particular data do not fit his general
findings. When, for instance, he finds that Poland is an overachiever despite low $n$
Achievement scores in the readers, he writes: "A recheck of the readers used . . .
suggests that they may not have been representative," since trade books of children's
stories rather than schoolbooks had been used. When he finds that Turkey has rapid
economic growth, high reader $n$ Achievement levels, but low $n$ Achievement among
managers, he writes: "We can reasonably infer that the schoolbooks may be atypically
high in $n$ Achievement." David C. McClelland, *The Achieving Society* (Princeton:
Van Nostrand, 1961), pp. 101, 266.
[27] *Ibid.*, p. 75.

criteria of selection are used by those who must decide to adopt
or not to adopt for classroom use a particular set of stories? As
Los Angeles teachers learned in the decade after World War II,
when they decided to adopt UNESCO readers for their students,
the question of the criteria of selection can become a very touchy
issue in the community at large. Second—and this may be a minor
consideration—the process by which textbooks are prepared for
school use is more complicated than McClelland suggests. There
are several factors that help to determine what readers a committee of the school board may choose among: contracts between
publishers and particular writers; copyrights and copyright in-
fringements; production costs; marketing considerations; regional
differentiation (e.g., how likely is it that a textbook manufacturer
will be able to sell to a school board in Mississippi a reader which
pictures white and Negro children playing together?); personal
relationships between salesmen and school board members in particular areas; and so forth. Even the reader most representative of
cultural values can easily fall into a trap somewhere along this
route.

McClelland then raises "the theoretical issue as to whether
fantasy reflects what a person has or doesn't have."[28] Although
there are good reasons why either alternative should be true, I
am not aware of any research that settles the question finally.
Research on $n$ Affiliation performed by McClelland's associates is
instructive in this regard. They asked two groups of college
freshmen—the first comprising men who had just been accepted
into social fraternities, and the second consisting in men who had
been rejected despite their desire to join a fraternity, and who had
afterward expressed their disappointment to the dean—to write
short stories describing what was probably happening in a picture
flashed before them on a screen. It turned out that the level of
$n$ Affiliation in stories by rejected subjects was almost twice as
high as that in the stories of their more socially accepted colleagues. These data cannot answer the question conclusively, but
they do suggest that social rejection is associated with $n$ Affiliation
(unless there is an intervening variable that accounts for both).
Whether this relationship—non-affiliation (social rejection) and $n$
Affiliation—holds true for a person's sense of having achieved
something and his $n$ Achievement score is something that remains

[28] *Ibid.*, p. 76.

to be seen. As McClelland points out, "it is impossible to decide on theoretical grounds which of these two alternatives is most likely."[29]

Another major problem pertains to the values themselves as they are portrayed in the children's readers. Even if we assume that the author has played the role of cultural bridge properly, we must ask, along with McClelland, "of what or of whom" the values are typical. Do they represent values typical of the culture as a whole or of specific subcultures (e.g., the intellectual elite)? Do they represent the values actually held by most of the people in the culture or just the "best" values that they want transmitted to children? Or do they even comprise a set of values that a ministry of education is trying to inculcate in a population? Given the sampling process used, there is no simple answer to such questions. McClelland has pointed to several problematical examples—the fact that Algerian and Tunisian readers, although dealing with North African themes, were printed in Paris; the fact that Soviet readers of the 1920's dealt with values clearly not held by the masses of peasants; the fact that Argentine readers in the post-World War II years had "a very strong political slant in that most of the stories glorified the then dictator Juan Peron"[30]—and it is not difficult to think of others. American civics texts, for example, emphasize the value of individual political participation but, as may be seen by the level of participation (other than voting) in any national or state or local election, this value is not shared in practice by most Americans.

McClelland's efforts to date to discover of what or of whom the readers are "typical" in a national culture have not been very satisfactory. A national sample survey of Catholic and Protestant students in the United States offered some confirmation of the thesis that values in readers are typical of more generally held cultural values. Less representative but cross-national surveys, however, have held out less hope. In countries where readers were low on the $n$ Achievement scale, students scored high in projective tests for levels of $n$ Achievement, and vice versa. McClelland rejects the conclusion that such findings cast doubt upon the validity of reader $n$ Achievement scores as indicators of cultural values. Instead, he suggests that these findings show that

[29] *Ibid.*
[30] *Ibid.*, p. 101.

reader scores may not reflect *n* Achievement levels in *any* group of individuals in the country: in this sense any comparison with individual scores is invalid or unrepresentative. Rather, the reader stress on achievement *may represent something more like "national aspirations"*—the tendency of people in public (e.g., in children's textbooks) to think about achievement.[31]

In short, after data or their absence have failed to confirm other interpretations of his representational model, McClelland falls back upon the conclusion that the readers must represent the totality of the culture which produced them.

But McClelland is obviously not happy with this conclusion. His final statement on his representational model is illuminating:

> Comparison of reader *n* Achievement levels with levels obtained from individuals has raised some interesting questions as to just what the readers are measuring. It has even thrown some doubt on whether they are measuring anything of importance, but in the end, the proof of the pudding is in the eating: do they enable us to predict which countries will develop more rapidly economically?[32]

That the readers do enable such predictions—at least to McClelland's satisfaction, if not always to that of others—does not get around the fact that his argument begs the key question of the representational model.

*Angell: Social Values of Soviet and American Elites.* The study focuses on social values held by segments of the Soviet and American elites, with particular attention paid to values important in the foreign policy making process. Values are defined as perceptual images, that is, elements "of the good life as seen by the person who cherishes" them.[33] Of the six elite groups identified as being most relevant for the two societies, four are fairly comparable: military, scientific, cultural, and labor elites. The remaining two elite groups in the Soviet Union are the government-Party elite and the economic elite, in the United States the cosmopolitan elite and the provincial elite. Angell selected the following publications as representative of the various elites:

[31] *Ibid.,* p. 79, italics added. Later on, McClelland adds that "the 1950 finding suggests . . . that *n* Achievement levels in children's readers are more of a reflection of the mood or motivational level of a nation at the time than an educational influence which is affecting the next generation." *Ibid.,* p. 101.

[32] *Ibid.,* p. 79.

[33] Robert C. Angell, "Social Values of Soviet and American Elites: Content Analysis of Elite Media," *Journal of Conflict Resolution,* VIII (1964), 330.

*United States*
  Cosmopolitan        *New York Times, Fortune*
  Provincial           *Nation's Business, American Bar Associa-*
                              *tion Journal*
  Labor                 *American Federationist*
  Military            *Army, Navy, Air Force*
  Scientific           *Science, American Scientist, GeoTimes,*
                              *American Institute of Biological Sci-*
                              *ences Bulletin, Chemical & Engineering*
                              *News, Physics Today, Bulletin of the*
                              *Atomic Scientists*
  Cultural            *Saturday Review, Harpers*
*Soviet Union*
  Government-Party   *Pravda, Kommunist, Voprosy Filosofii*
  Economic          *Voprosy Ekonomikii, Sovetskaia Torgovlia,*
                              *Planovoe Khozaistvo*
  Labor                 *Sotsialisticheskii Trud*
  Military            *Krasnaia Zvezda*
  Scientific           *Vestnik Akademii Nauk, Vestnik Vysshei*
                              *Shkoly*
  Cultural            *Novyi Mir, Literaturnaia Gazeta, Teatr*

The period covered is from May 1, 1957 to April 30, 1960—a three-year period of relative peace and quiet in Soviet-American relations. The frequency of *positions taken by or attributed to the various elite groups* in these publications was tabulated, intercountry variations in positions were systematically examined, and some attention was given to intra-country variations in value positions.

Three types of problems arose in the selection of the sample. First, there was the question of the size of the sample for each publication. Angell decided to allot "roughly equal reading time . . . to the periodicals for each of the six elites," but, if anything, more effort should be put into analyzing Soviet journals since "we felt we already knew much more about American than about Soviet society."[34] He does not give information about the reasons for the particular sampling design chosen—e.g., every 22nd daily issue of *Pravda* but every 43rd daily issue of the military journal *Krasnaia Zvezda*. A second problem was the paucity of value

[34] *Ibid.*, p. 336.

statements in some sources. This was particularly the case with American scientific journals:

> It was not intended originally to use so many of them, but when it became apparent that *Science* and *The American Scientist* were going to yield so little, it was necessary to find more specialized scientific periodicals that had some editorial or editorial-like material. *The Bulletin of the Atomic Scientists* is much the richest in the kind of material desired, but only a small sample was taken here because the scientists who support the journal are regarded by other scientists as not wholly representative of the profession.[35]

Third, the question of what to read was important. In some American cases (e.g., the *New York Times*) it was thought sufficient to analyze only editorials; except for specific categories of items (e.g., obituaries, "articles of an exclusively historical character not giving value preferences in the period studied"), everything in the Soviet publications was included in the analysis.

The representational model in Angell's study is, in essence, merely an extension of the "prestige papers" idea, except that it explicitly rejects any inferences about the readers of the journals. Angell nonetheless compounds the problem faced by Pool and others by assuming that individual publications are representative of separate elites in Soviet and American life. Even if we are willing to accept the *New York Times* as indicative of "elite attitudes," we may well be unwilling to agree that the *American Bar Association Journal* is indicative of any attitudes other than those of the men writing its editorials. It may still be possible to view the distribution of values in all the American publications taken together as somehow an indicator of values held by a broad stratum of American elite groupings; similarly, the entire collection of Soviet journals may give us a better idea of Soviet elite values than would one "prestige paper" by itself.[36]

Angell's analysis raises an interesting question about intra-country variations in totalitarian societies. He writes:

> enough free play has developed near the top of Soviet society since the

---

[35] *Ibid.*; this statement underlines the necessity for making the research and sampling design more explicit than was done, for it suggests that the journals were weighted somehow according to their "representativeness."

[36] It is interesting in this regard that Angell gives less space to intra-country than to intercountry variations; his data nonetheless present interesting possibilities for analyses of within-nation differences.

> death of Stalin for elite differences of value to come to light in Soviet periodicals. It is true that the explicit differences on the Soviet side are not striking, but in a good many of our value dimensions they are real.[37]

To what extent may we expect publicly expressed attitudes, beliefs, and values to be different in various Soviet "elite" publications? If we expect uniformity (the monolithic hypothesis) and discover differences, must we revise our estimate of an enslaved press? Or if we expect differences (the pluralist hypothesis) and find them, is our expectation confirmed? Unfortunately, if all we have access to is Angell's data, we must respond negatively to both these latter questions. What is needed to test the alternative hypotheses is time-series data to establish the changing limits of acceptable differences in a totalitarian society: we need to know whether the level of intra-country variation is now greater, lesser, or about the same as it was during Stalin's heyday.

Finally, in reviewing Angell's study, we must ask if it is proper to accept for analytical purposes views attributed to one elite by members of another. Before we can consider such evidence, it is necessary to know, for instance, how reliable an estimate of "the military mind" is likely to be found in the editorial columns of the *Bulletin of the Atomic Scientists*, or how accurately writers in *GeoTimes* will reflect the mood of America's cultural elite. Fortunately, Angell clearly recognizes the danger of misinterpretation due to such attributions, and even keeps the attributed value positions separate from the direct assertions in his tables and analyses.

### Validating Representational Models: A Plea for Future Research

The bulk of my remarks to this point have been critical. In concentrating on the weaker aspects of some of the recent cross-national content analyses, however, I do not mean to suggest that the analyses themselves have been without merit. But the fact that their results have been both interesting and fruitful in terms of generating hypotheses about political behavior does not hide the fact that their theoretical underpinnings and assumptions have often been insufficiently examined. Perhaps the time has come for content analysts to look again at their research tools, just as survey researchers in the 1940's and early 1950's turned their attention to

[37] *Ibid.*, p. 335.

some procedures that many of them had come to take for granted. The following list of specific and feasible research tasks is certainly not exhaustive, but it may serve as a beginning.

1. We need intensive analyses of a wide variety of publications in each country that is of interest to us. What we want to know is the range of attitudes, perceptions, and values expressed in these media on a variety of variables over time. If we had such information, it would be possible for a researcher to specify that for a particular analysis he wants to examine a publication that is, let us say, pro-labor but otherwise conservative on economic matters and liberal politically; or a conservative political journal with avant garde attitudes on culture; or a newspaper that, on a given range of variables, is "typical" of all newspapers in the country; or a journal that became progressively more liberal over time.

2. It would be possible to compare such empirically-based delineations of media characteristics with the ratings of knowledgeable judges on the same dimensions. For some purposes it may turn out that judgmental ratings are sufficiently accurate; or we may find that judges with certain types of background are most qualified to rate the press on certain dimensions.

3. We need to pay closer attention to readership surveys, such as those conducted for advertising purposes, to get an idea of the audience of particular publications. It should be possible, for instance, to find out approximately how many people with high professional and socio-economic status report that they read the *New York Times*, *Nation*, or *Life*. Looked at from the other direction, it should be possible, after getting estimates of the number of members of a particular elite grouping, to determine what percentage of that number reads a particular journal.

4. Closely related to this is the need to utilize both intensive and extensive survey research to determine the extent to which people's views—attitudes, perceptions, values—parallel those presented in the publications they read regularly. Note that here I am asking for the delineation of an empirical relationship rather than inquiring into causality (i.e., does the reader read the publication because it reflects his views? or does the periodical shape his views? or is the true relationship a bit of both?).

5. It would be useful to have corroborative evidence of an aggregate nature for a content analysis. Examples of such evidence might include public opinion anaylsis, elite interviews, content analysis of other types of messages, and other indicators of be-

havior.[38] Ideally, of course, for any research project we would like to use all indicators available, bringing them to bear upon the aspect of behavior in which we are interested. For instance, if we are interested in the development of Western European attitudes toward arms control and disarmament, all the above types of evidence could serve as independent indicators of different aspects of Western European decision-making processes.

6. Turning from inferences about antecedent events (WHY, WHO) to inferences about consequent events (WHOM, WHAT EFFECT), there is a crying need to integrate social psychological data on attitude change with the theory of content analysis. What is the function of an attitude for an individual? What conditions maximize the impact of a written communication on a person's attitudes, perceptions, and values? (For example, what role does the person's previous level of informtaion play? Or his commitment to a particular ideology?) How important is written communication relative to an individual's face-to-face communications network?

7. It should also be possible to undertake intensive interviews with a wide variety of elite groupings to ascertain the extent to which their members report that they are influenced by particular media. Do they look to these media for authoritative information and ready-made views? What other sources influence them? Are the particular media in which we are interested more or less important than the other sources of information and attitudes?

8. For cross-national research the question of functional equivalence is crucial. The task is to find sets of messages that perform approximately the same function in all the societies included in the analysis and that are capable of being analyzed using the same set of research tools. Some differences are ones of format: The *New York Times* and *The Times* of London have clearcut editorials

---

[38] One approach is suggested by Ole R. Holsti and Robert C. North, "Comparative Data from Content Analysis: Perceptions of Hostility and Economic Variables in the 1914 Crisis," in Richard L. Merritt and Stein Rokkan (eds.), *Comparing Nations: The Use of Quantitative Data in Cross-National Research* (New Haven: Yale University Press, 1966), pp. 169-90. But in their comparison of perceptual data on conflict with "hard" data such as the flow of gold, stock market fluctuations, and commodity futures, other questions arise. If it is true that there is a strong correlation between the perceptual and the other data in the six critical weeks that led up to the outbreak of World War I, is it also true that perceptual data on conflict would correlate with the "hard" data in times of peace or in times of a severe financial crisis? If there is a high degree of correlation in all such circumstances, why bother with the arduous task of collecting the perceptual data? Using Lazarsfeld's concept of the interchangeability of indicators, would it not be simpler (and cheaper in terms of research time and resources) to use the "hard" data as indicators of perceived conflict?

on a variety of issues, for instance, whereas *Le Monde* usually carries only one editorial (on foreign policy) and the *Frankfurter allgemeine Zeitung* relies mainly on signed, editorialized news columns. Other differences are more fundamental. What is the level of party partisanship in the press? What is the national ethic about an independent and "objective" press? How widely read by the opposition are "prestige papers"? What effect does the literacy level of a country have upon the nature and influence of its press? What is the difference between "elite" and "mass" newspapers in different countries? What is the difference in press attitudes between countries with regional newspapers and countries with national newspapers (e.g., between the United States and Great Britain)? How comparable is the press in totalitarian and democratic societies? What are the bounds of permissible disagreement in the different media of a communist state? What effect does a change in government have upon the press of various countries? Questions such as these, I might add, are fairly simply answered for European countries, but grow extremely complex when we try to account for media in non-Western areas.[39]

The research tasks that I am proposing are basic. They will not produce glamorous results that will dazzle the eyes of our colleagues and lay a golden path to foundation support. But they will serve to give a firmer foundation to cross-national research using content analysis.

---

[39] Another severe problem is the functional equivalence of units of analysis (e.g., words, which may have different meanings over space and over time).

# 2. Statistical Techniques

# 2. Statistical Techniques

## Introductory Note

*"la carrière ouverte aux talens"—Napoleon*

The author offers seven statistical techniques applicable in political science. Factor analysis is a device for data analysis which has already received considerable attention in political science research.[1] Power spectrum analysis appears applicable to research involving observation of data in a time series, such as election returns.[2] Cluster analysis or numerical taxonomy may be applied to the testing of hypotheses regarding influence relationships in groups.[3] General linear hypothesis is a technique for discerning causal inferences. It may, the author notes, test the hypothesis that religion is a significant variable in explaining political contributions by corporate executives. To use an example suggested by Hayward Alker, it may test the hypothesis that a high level of voter participation stimulates a high level of government expenditures (or the reverse).[4]

In considering statistical devices appropriate for predictive models of decision-making, Carl Kossack discusses simultaneous linear regression. His economic example, the relation of price and quantity, suggests analogous political applications (i.e., Alker's voter participation-government activity nexus). Simultaneous equations are useful here because we are not certain which is the independent variable and which the dependent variable.[5]

Response surface analysis includes a variety of statistical procedures which may be utilized to discern "the best operating con-

---

[1] See, for example, Hoyward R. Alker, Jr., "Dimensions of Conflict in the General Assembly," *American Political Science Review*, LVIII, (September, 1964), 642-57.

S. Sidney Ulmer uses the modified factor analysis developed by McQuitty to analyze behavior of judges. See Ulmer, "The Analysis of Behavior Patterns in the United States Supreme Court," *Journal of Politics*, XXII (1960), 629-53. See also L. L. McQuitty, "Elementary Factor Analysis," *Psychological Reports*, IX (1951), 71-78, and see his "Elementary Linkage Analysis for Isolating Both Orthogonal Types and Typal Relevances," *Educational and Psychological Measurement*, XVII (1957), 207-29.

[2] Cf. Donald E. Stokes, "A Variance Components Model of Political Effects," in John M. Claunch (ed.), *Mathematical Applications in Political Science*, (Dallas: Arnold Foundation Monographs, Southern Methodist University, 1965), pp. 61-85.

[3] See the cluster analysis technique employed by Ulmer, "The Analysis of Behavior Patterns in the United States Supreme Court," *Journal of Politics*, XXII (1960), 629-53.

[4] *Mathematics and Politics* (New York: Macmillan, 1965), p. 66.

[5] *Ibid.*, pp. 68-73.

ditions for a system." The canvassing resource allocation problem, discussed by Kramer in this volume, comes immediately to mind. The techniques discussed by Kossack are designed to yield optimum operational conditions to inform the decision-maker in planning and in the use of resources.

Classification techniques, the final procedures noted by Kossack, have a variety of practical applications to politics, particularly in the field of administration. The author uses the example of an admissions problem in a college: evaluating prospective students by means of high-school grades and a battery of test scores. The problem requires that similar data on a previous population of students and actual college performance by these students be correlated in order to estimate the likelihood of the *new* student population completing the college curricula. A useful and realistic classification system may be constructed when the model is applied to the earlier experience.

# Statistical Analysis, The Computer and Political Science Research

CARL F. KOSSACK

*University of Georgia*

## INTRODUCTION

As our society becomes more and more complex, the need for sophisticated methods of analysis through which one can study problems associated with various activities becomes more and more evident. This need is present not only in the biological and physical sciences but also in the social and political sciences. In fact, one can successfully argue that in the so-called soft-sciences the need is increasing at an even more rapid rate than in the hard-sciences. Our social and political systems have become increasingly more complex, with higher order interactions playing a role today that was unknown in the earlier rural society of the past.

Since one of the approaches considered by statisticians is that of inductive reasoning—making valid conclusions from evidence contained in observational data—and since man's understanding of most political phenomena is such as to exclude the possibility of mathematical or stochastic modeling of the system, it seems appropriate to consider in this paper some of the recent advances that have been made in statistics, particularly as they relate to problems encountered in political science research. If one associates with these advance statistical applications the power of modern digital computers, it is now quite feasible to consider applications which one could not even dream about some ten years ago. One should also note that modern computers provide a technological bridge which can make available to the researcher analytical techniques which far exceed his in-house capabilities.

In considering the phases through which a scientific investigation usually advances, one possible classification of these phases would be:

*The Data Analysis Phase*—During this phase of a scientific inquiry, the researcher acquires observational data associated with the phenomenon being studied and "processes" these data in an attempt to discover important or interesting relationships within the data as well as to screen the data to eliminate errors along with non-discriminating variables or measurements. One of the most important statistical aspects to be considered during this phase is that of the sampling plan to be used during the collection of the data, since one not only is interested in having his data representative of the general situation but is also interested in the efficiency of his data collection procedures.

*The Hypothesis or Relationship Testing Phase*—After analyzing the initial set of data, the researcher progresses to the stage where he can generate hypotheses with regard to the phnomenon under study. Since these hypotheses generally were acquired using available observational data, it is required to test statistically such hypotheses. To do this it is generally necessary for one to develop an experimental design or sampling plan from which one efficiently acquires new data upon which such statistical tests of the hypotheses can be generated.

*The Decision-Making Phase*—Once a phenomenon is well enough understood, at least as far as its role in applied systems is concerned, interest centers on the use of this understanding of the phenomena to improve decision-making capabilities. In statistics, this type of activity falls under the general category of statistical decision theory as applied to complex systems. The natural outgrowth of system decision-making is that of stochastic modeling of the system, including the study of such models through the use of simulation techniques. In fact, many individuals feel that the ultimate objective of research is the formulation of a stochastic or probability model of the phenomenon under study and the use of such a model to improve one's decision-making capabilities.

It is not the intention of this paper to consider in depth the nature of scientific study, but simply to note the natural phases through which many such statistically oriented studies evolve.

## THE ROLE OF THE COMPUTER

It has been generally recognized that the modern digital computer has greatly enhanced man's ability to process data and to do scientific computing. In fact, it may be conservatively stated that in the last twenty years computational power has increased six orders of magnitude, indicating that in some respects whatever data processing was evolved in the 1940's can now be done a million times faster. Of real interest is how this increased capability will affect our scientific analyses in the future. This becomes especially important when one realizes that most problems of interest are multivariate, often involving the time variable. Until recently, most analyses were unable to cope adequately with such dynamic multivariate problems, and thus the researcher had to be satisfied with analyses that involved fairly restrictive assumptions. It is only natural to expect that some of the increased computational power available in the modern high-speed digital computer will be harnessed so as to reduce dramatically these restrictive assumptions.

Still another aspect of modern computers is their ability to use internally stored programs. This means that sophisticated analyses, once they are programmed, can be made available to individuals all over the world. This capability should enable us to bridge the technological gap that exists between modern theory and practice. It is to be expected that the emerging sciences should find it possible to take advantage of theories and techniques that have been evolved in the more established fields without having to go through the long evolutionary mathematical process required in the past.

These two aspects of modern scientific computers challenges one to consider how advanced statistical techniques may be introduced into scientific disciplines in a fashion that would enable one to apply these new techniques to his particular research problem with the minimum of difficulty.

## ADVANCED STATISTICAL APPLICATIONS

I have reviewed the recent statistical literature and have selected from the new techniques found in the literature those which appear to be most promising, keeping in mind the dynamic-multivariate nature of most applied research problems and the capability of modern digital computers. In the remainder of this paper, I would like to discuss briefly seven such advanced techniques. In these discussions, I will try to follow a regular pattern; (a) the type of problem for which the technique is appropriate, (b) how the technique "solves" the problem, (c) what are the general advantages in utilizing a computer when applying the technique, and (d) a small list of appropriate references.

The techniques selected are:

*Data Analysis*

    I.  Factor Analysis

    II.  Power Spectrum Analysis

*Hypothesis Testing*
    III.   Cluster Analysis — Numerical Taxonomy
    IV.   General Linear Hypothesis
*Decision Making*
    V.   Simultaneous Regression
    VI.   Response Surface Analysis
    VII.   Classification Techniques

## I. FACTOR ANALYSIS

In factor analysis, one is concerned with how to account for the observed correlation among all the observed variables associated with the phenomenon under study in terms of the smallest number of factors and the smallest residual error. In many respects, the problem considered by a factor analysis is that of attempting to reduce the number of variables needed to describe a phenomenon. It is recognized that if one indiscriminately adds more variables to his observational vector the law of diminishing return sets in, and soon one is losing rather than gaining information because of the noise introduced by the additional variables. Thus, one would like to find a new set of variables (factors) which are essentially uncorrelated, each of which adds significantly to the information.

In the analysis, no distinction is made between so-called independent and dependent variables, since prediction is not a consideration. Thus, while in regression the constants found as regression coefficients are merely constants used in the prediction, in factor analysis the constants obtained suffer from the demand that the weights they give to the derived variables must admit to interpretation and the derived variables must have a scientifically meaningful interpretation. Fundamentally, the object is to discover whether the variables can be made to exhibit some underlying order that may throw light on the processes that produce the individual differences shown in all the variables.

In a factor analysis, the basic mathematical model is
$$S_{ji} = C_{j1}x_{1i} + C_{j2}x_{2i} + \ldots + C_{jq}x_{qi} + \ldots + C_{jq}x_{qi}$$
where $S_{ji}$ is the "score" (measure) made by the $i^{th}$ individual on the $j^{th}$ "test" (variable)
$x_{qi}$ is the measure for the $i^{th}$ individual on the $q^{th}$ factor (uncorrelated reference ability)
and $C_{jq}$ is the weight given the $q^{th}$ factor relative to the $j^{th}$ variable

To determine the weightings, the $C_{jq}$'s, the correlation matrix of the original observational variables is "factored." The mathematical problem associated with this factoring, since factoring is not unique, is to make the factoring such that the smallest number of interpretable factors are used, leaving an insignificant unexplained residual. It is evident that such a technique requires judgment on the part of the investigator, and, in fact, the several different methods of factoring the correlation matrix appear to yield different levels of effectiveness, depending on the particular type of problem being considered.

The most common solution which has been programmed for digital computers is that which is called the principal component solution coupled with an orthogonal rotation of the factor matrix. Input data for such programs usually are in the form of raw data, but may simply be the resulting inter-correlation matrix. Included in the output of most computer programs is the initial factor matrix which is simply the coefficients $C_{jq}$ and the orthogonal rotated factor matrix. The satisfactory nature of the solution depends upon the ability of the analyst to interpret the factors effectively, considering their loadings relative to the original variables.

The power of the .digital computer to perform a factor analysis is clearly indicated when one considers that there exists a program which will handle up to 80 variables with up to 10,000 cases (individuals) using as little as an hour of running time for this size problem. In fact, without a computer, a problem of this magnitude simply could not be analyzed.

## II. Power Spectrum Analysis

One frequently obtains observations that are in the form of a continuous or discrete time series. Often such series are of a type that is called stationary. By this we mean that, if a random sampling is made from the time series with equal times between observations obtaining the sequence of observations $x_1, x_2, x_3, ..., x_t..., x_n$, these x's are such that for all t's $E(x_t) = \mu$, the variance of $x_t = V_o$, and the covariance $(x_t, x_{t+s}) = V_s$ for all integer s. Of particular importance is the fact that the covariance between two observations $x_t$ and $x_{t+s}$ depend only on the time separation s and not on the clock time t. One should recall that the covariance $(x_t, x_{t+s})$ is defined as

$$\text{Cov}(x_t, x_{t+s}) = E\left[ (x_t - \mu_t)(x_{t+s} - \mu_{t+s}) \right] = r_{x_t, x_{t+s}} \, \sigma_{x_t} \, \sigma_{x_{t+s}}.$$

Thus a stationary time series is such that the correlation between two observations does not depend upon where one takes the observations but only on how far apart the two observations are. We really are dealing with a signal that exhibits periodicity over time rather than dynamic change. The problem associated with the analysis of such stationary time series is to convert the analogue signal into quantitative values which will then admit more readily to mathematical analysis.

Since the time series is periodic, it seems natural to assume that the signal is a composite of several cosine functions of varying frequency and amplitude. Along with these cosine functions one assumes that there is superimposed a random noise factor. Thus, one can hope to decompose the time series into the significant cosine functions and to replace the continuous set of data with a finite number of frequencies and associated amplitudes of these cosine functions. These frequencies and amplitudes can then be used in pattern recognition type problems so as to be able more readily to recognize patterns in the signal and to be able to distinguish between signals coming from different underlying conditions or sources.

In solving this decomposition problem through the use of a power spectrum analysis, one formally considers that the signal is given as a function of time, say $x(t)$. Then the auto covariance function is defined by

$$C(\tau) = \lim_{T \to \infty} \frac{1}{T} \int_{-T/2}^{+T/2} x(t) \, x(t + \tau) \, dt$$

and the power spectrum frequency is given by

$$P(f) = \lim_{T \to \infty} \frac{1}{T} \left[ \int_{T/2}^{T/2} x(t) e^{-i2\pi ft} \, dt \right]^2$$

Now if the signal $x(t)$ corresponds closely with the function $\cos 2\pi ft$, the value of $P(f)$ is large, while if the signal fails to correspond, $P(f)$ will be small. In fact, if there is actually no correspondence, $P(f)$, though theoretically zero, would exhibit some positive value due to the random noise entering the evaluation. Pictorially we could represent the stationary time series by the following figure:

x(t)

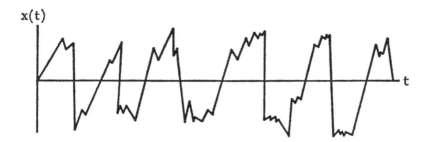

The power spectrum of such a time series could be represented by
the following figure:

P(f)

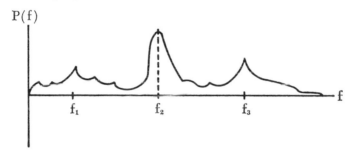

In the above representation, it may be recognized that the original
signal is a composite consisting namely of three sinusoidal functions with frequencies $f_1$, $f_2$, and $f_3$ with amplitudes whose squares
(power) correspond to the heights of three peaks exhibited on
the power spectrum graph.

In practice, the problem of estimating the power spectrum
through the use of digital computers requires first that one replace
the infinite range considered in the theory by a finite range. Now,
it is apparent that the restriction on the range of the data used
restricts the frequency range for which one can obtain estimates.
The lowest practical frequency that can be estimated corresponds
to one-half the range use. Next, one must replace the continuous
analogue signal with isolated sampled points. The sampling rate
used also imposes a restriction on the range of frequencies that
can be studied, since the highest frequency about which one will
have information is $\pi/k$, where k is the length of time between
sampled points. Unfortunately, the desire to take a longer range
of data with more frequent samplings is usually thwarted by lack
of sufficient data and/or the lack of computer energy to analyze

the multiplicity of points generated by a high sampling rate.

In the computer programming of a power spectrum analysis, the dimensions of the program depend on the size of the computer being used; but for a large-size computer, programs exist that can handle up to 20 different series with up to 1,000 discrete data points per series. In computing, the autocorrelations up to 200 lags can be considered. Not only does the output of the program include a plot of the input data, the autocorrelation function, and printed and plotted power spectral estmiates, but one is enabled to examine the interrelationship between two series by having the computer determine and print out the cross-covariance and the "coherence function" for any pair of signals from the several series used as input for the program.

### III. Cluster Analysis or Numerical Taxonomy

In many investigations, the amount of information obtained about each individual and the number of individuals studied are so large that the investigator finds it difficult to know where to start his analysis. Since one of the purposes of science is to generalize, one often would like to group individuals together into more or less homogeneous groups relative to the several measurements that have been made on each individual. At the same time, it may be of interest to differentiate between the numerous variables as to those which provide discriminatory power in separating off such groups.

A cluster analysis or numerical taxonomy program is designed to uncover statistical similarities within the data, to form clusters of the most similar cases, and to select those attributes which are statistically more important in determining the classification derived through this method. With the large mass of data and the many observations from each individual, the problem is to identify a few main classes of data rather than the many individual cases. Technically, one may argue that the data represents a mixture of samples from several distinct populations and that one is interested in sorting the observations into their respective population groups without even knowing how many populations are involved. In some respects the technique could be called statistical sorting.

In most numerical taxonomy programs, the analysis is approached by first converting the data into attributes. That is, the information is reduced to a set of variables which can take on only the values zero or one. It is apparent that both quantitative and qualitative data can be converted into attributes, since the attribute concept is essentially the basis behind all information. Thus, for categorical type data, each possible class from a given category can be made an attribute variable with the zero indicating the individual is not in the class and the one indicating the individual is in the class. In the case of measured variables, the range can be subdivided into many subranges and each subrange be considered as an attribute variable.

The analysis then generates a similarity coefficient which essentially indicates which observations have essentially the same attribute structure. Thus we may use

$$S_{i,j} = M_{i,j} / N_{i,j}$$

where $M_{i,j}$ repersents the number of attributes possessed in common by cases i and j, while $N_{i,j}$ represents the number of attributes possessed by either of them. The similarity ratio $S_{i,j}$ could be considered as the weighted probability in finding a matching attribute between the two individuals for any characteristics selected at random. Hence, a very large value of S would indicate a much greater degree of similarity between the two cases than is likely with random distribution of the attributes. Similarly, a very low value of S would indicate a non-random divergence of characteristics between the two cases.

In order to measure roughly how "typical" a case is, a count, $R_i$, is made of the number of other cases with which the case in question has at least one attribute in common. Finally, a measure H is made for each case by multiplying together all the non-zero R values of S for each case. Thus,

$$H_i = S_{i1} \times S_{i2} \times S_{i3} \times \ldots \times S_{i,n}$$

Here $H_i$ can be thought of as representing the probability, for any characteristic selected at random of those attributes processed by case i, that all other of the non-zero R cases would also possess the attribute. We have for each case two measures of typicality, $R_i$ and $H_i$, where $H_i$ can be considered as a refined measure that could be used to differentiate cases with the same R.

Thus, one may rank the cases first by descending values of R and then by descending values of H within each value of R. The first case listed can then be considered as the center of the first population grouping and other members of the cluster are then identified by high values of S in conjunction with this nodal case. The problem of where to cut off the cluster must be resolved either by using judgment or by the ordered listing of (R,H)'s.

One may decide that the second cluster center should be taken to be the individual who is at some predetermined rank within the table. When that case is found in the ordering of S's around the first cluster center, the cluster is truncated and a new cluster determined around the new center using the S's associated with the remaining cases and the new nodal case. Thus, the clustering can continue until all cases are sorted into one of the clusters.

The entire approach to numerical taxonomy makes the use of a high-speed digital computer most appropriate. The many logical comparisons and testings made in deriving values for M,N,S,R, and H are operations which a computer handles· naturally. The sheer volume of the operations also requires a processing speed found only in electronic computers. For example, if there are only 100 cases in the collection, then 4,950 values each of M,N, and S must be calculated for every analysis made with new or revised information. The basic approach described above is quite suitable for programming for most types of computers.

## IV. General Linear Hypothesis

In experimental situations it is common to analyze multiresponse experimental data using the appropriate univariate analysis on each response. However, there is often an interdependency between these responses which would be ignored by this single-response-at-a-time approach. At the same time, the various univariate analyses that one may elect to use depending upon the circumstances of the experiment, and even when considered separately, involve the analysis of some underlying mathematical model, including both the estimation of parameters and the testing of hypotheses associated with the model. The "general linear hypothesis" concept combines these mathematical models into a single general model enabling one to use a single analytical approach to such problems and at the same time to handle the multiresponse problem.

It seems best to introduce the general linear hypothesis concept in the single response variable case and then to discuss its generalization to multi-response type analyses. An attempt will be made to show how the general linear hypothesis model includes the analysis of variance, regression, and the analysis of covariance as special cases.

In an attempt to show the generality of the model and the power of the matrix notation, the generalized linear model concept will

be summarized in matrix form and then the model will be applied to one or more of the special cases noted above, expanding the expressions into a non-matrix notation. A mathematical model must first be evolved showing how one feels the response variable (dependent variable) relates to the design variables (independent variables). In the general linear case, we have the model*
$y = A\xi + e.$

This model reduces to the following special cases:

i) The analysis of variance model (simple two-way design)

$$y_{ij} = \mu + \tau_i + \nu_j + e_{ij}$$

where $\tau_i$ is the $i^{th}$ treatment effect, $\nu_j$ is the $j^{th}$ block effect, $\mu$ = the overall mean and $e_{ij}$ the experimental error.

ii) The regression model (multiple linear regression)

$$y_i = \mu + .\beta_1 x_{1i} + \beta_2 x_{2i} + \ldots + \beta_r x_{ri} + e_i$$

iii) The analysis of covarience model (simple two-way design)

$$y_{ij} = \mu + \tau_i + \nu_j + \beta_1 x_{1,ij} + \beta_2 x_{2,ij} + \ldots + \beta_r x_{r,ij} + e_{ij}$$

To demonstrate how the general model reduces to these special models, consider the regression case. Then $y = A\xi + e$ can be written in expanded form as:

$$
\begin{bmatrix} y_1 \\ y_2 \\ \cdot \\ \cdot \\ \cdot \\ y_n \end{bmatrix}
=
\begin{bmatrix}
1 & x_{11} & x_{12} & \ldots & x_{1r} \\
1 & x_{21} & x_{22} & \ldots & x_{2r} \\
- & - & - & & - \\
- & - & - & & - \\
- & - & - & & - \\
1 & x_{n1} & x_{n2} & \ldots & x_{nr}
\end{bmatrix}
\begin{bmatrix} \mu \\ B_1 \\ B_2 \\ \cdot \\ \cdot \\ B_r \end{bmatrix}
+
\begin{bmatrix} e_1 \\ e_2 \\ \cdot \\ \cdot \\ \cdot \\ e_n \end{bmatrix}
$$

Expanding the expression for the $i^{th}$ element yields the form given under (ii) above.

Associated with any mathematical model is a set of hypotheses regarding the values of the parameters $\xi$ which are the unknown constants of interest in the study. In a linear hypothesis approach, these hypotheses must be expressible as linear relationships involving $\xi$'s and known coefficients. We thus have in the general case the set of linear hypotheses expressed as

$C\xi = O$

where C is a known matrix of coefficients.

To illustrate again the applicability of the general expression to

---

*An italic lower case letter indicates a vector, while an upper case letter indicates a matrix.

the special cases, we have for typical types of hypotheses the following:

i)   The analysis of variance model

$$\tau_1 = \tau_2 = \ldots = \tau_i$$

The hypothesis that a certain set of the treatment effects are all equal.

ii)  The regression model

$$\beta_{r-s-1} = \beta_{r-s-2} = \ldots = \beta_r = 0$$

The hypothesis that the last s independent variables have no linear relationship with the dependent variables when considered with the other r-s variables,

iii) Analysis of covariance model

$$\tau_1 = \tau_2 \ldots = \tau_t$$
$$\beta_{r-s-1} = \beta_{r-s-2} = \ldots = \beta_r = 0$$

A combination of the hypotheses introduced under (i) and (ii).

Before the given set of hypotheses can be statistically tested, one must first estimate the parameters, $\xi$, using the available experimental data. These estimates are given general form by

$$\xi = (A'A)^{-1} A'y$$

where the prime indicates the transpose of the given matrix and ( )$^{-1}$ indicates its inverse. In the special cases these estimates reduce to the familiar least squares estimates. Thus in regression

$$\hat{\beta}_i = \frac{\sum\limits_{j=1}^{n} (y_y - \bar{y}_i)(x_{ij} - \bar{x}_j)}{\sum\limits_{j=1}^{n} (x_{ij} - \bar{x}_j)^2}$$

The testing of the hypotheses is accomplished by using a test statistic in the form

$$F(n_h, n_e) = \frac{SSH/n_h}{SSE/n_e}$$

where $SSH = (C\xi)[C(A'A)^{-1}C']^{-1} C\hat{\xi}$

and $SSE = y'y - \xi'A'y$

The statistic $F(n_h, n_e)$ is the Snedecor F statistic with $n_h$ and $n_e$ representing the degrees of freedom for the hypothesis and error respectively. An alternative statistic that can be used is the Beta statistic defined by

$$\beta \left( \frac{m_e}{2}, \frac{m_h}{2} \right) = SSE/(SSH + SSE)$$

The hypothesis is then rejected for significantly low values of $\beta$.

Now, if the response is a vector quantity rather than a single measure, the generalization is relatively straightforward; since, instead of considering singly $y$, we must consider the vector $(y_1, y_2, ..., y_p)$, and the general linear hypothesis must be written in the form

$$(y_1, y_2, ..., y_p) = A(\xi_1, \xi_2, ..., \xi_p) + (e_1, e_2, ..., e_p)$$

Thus, the vectors of observations, parameters and error terms all become matrices, and we can symbolically write the model as

$$Y = {}_\Lambda \Phi + E$$

The subsequent analysis of this generalized model generalizes in a rather straightforward fashion (See Poston).

In considering the implications of this theory to computer programming, one should realize that matrix algebra can be programmed for computers in a fairly straightforward fashion. In fact, several computer programming languages have been developed utilizing vectors and matrices as basic elements in the language (See Bargmann). Thus, the researcher having access to such a computer program can analyze a large class of experiments without having to develop separate techniques for each special case.

## V. SIMULTANEOUS LINEAR REGRESSION

Many problems arise that require the construction of a mathematical model that will represent the operation of a social, political, or economic system. From this model one is interested in predicting future events that will follow when one or more variables in the model are changed or determining what policy should be followed to give a desired result or outcome in the system. Or perhaps the purpose of the model is simply to describe the system in mathematical form.

Given a model, one of the major research problems is to estimate its parameters. When the model is not explicitly stated, one often has to resort to simulation studies to help make reasonable estimates; however, in the case of a system expressed by simultaneous linear equations, the parameter estimates can be mathematically determined. One of the important models of this type is that of multiple linear regression, where one assumes a single dependent variable is governed in a linear fashion by the levels of a number of other "independent" variables. Simultaneous linear regression can be considered as a generality of multiple regression to the following situation. In the multiple regression relation, one and only one variable in each equation may be chosen as the dependent variable, whose changes can be explained by those of the explanatory, or independent, variables. Very often this choice is arbitrary, since economic and social relationships are not normally formulated in a simple manner. A typical example from economics would be price and quantity for a product. Surely one would be hard pressed to determine which to call dependent if the two occur in a set of additional "independent" variables. In fact, even if such a designation were made, the multiple linear regression model would not be properly estimated.

In simultaneous linear regression, one is able to introduce as the model a system of simultaneous linear equations rather than a single regression equation. The system is termed the structural set of equations, since each equation relates to a fundamental aspect of the phenomena being studied. Each structural equation may have more than one dependent variable and a number of independent variables.

For example, one may have the following five equations in the structural set:[*]

$$y_1 = b_{12}y_2 + b_{15}y_5 + c_{13}z_3 + c_{14}z_4 + c_{10}$$
$$y_1 = b_{23}y_3 + b_{25}y_5 + c_{23}z_3 + c_{20}$$
$$y_2 = c_{32}z_2 + c_{34}z_4 + c_{30}$$
$$y_3 = b_{44}y_4 + c_{41}z_1 + c_{43}z_3 + c_{40}$$
$$y_4 = b_{55}y_5 + c_{53}z_3 + c_{50}$$

where the $y$'s are dependent variables, the $z$'s are independent variables, and the $b$'s and $c$'s are the corresponding regression coefficients.

Since there are several methods by which the regression coefficients in such a set of simultaneous regression equations can be estimated, computer programs vary as to which or how many of these methods are included. Thus, we may use:

---

[*] See M. A. Girshick and T. Haavelmo, "Statistical Analysis of the Demand For Food: Examples of Simultaneous Estimation of Structural Equations," *Econometrica*, XV (1947), 79-110.

(i) Single-equation least-squares where the estimations are obtained by considering each equation separately, assuming that for estimation purposes the first dependent variable in the equation is the dependent variable. Usually if this method is used the results are obtained for comparison purposes only.

(ii) Two-stage least-squares still uses the single equation approach, but in the first stage a correction is made in the estimates for all but one of the dependent variables in the equation; and in the second stage, these corrected variables are used to compute the regression of the remaining dependent variables on all the other variables in the equation.

(iii) Limited-information estimation again uses the single equation approach, but, using the concept of maximum likelihood, treats all the dependent variables in the equation simultaneously.

(iv) Full-information estimation considers all the equations simultaneously and once again resorts to maximum likelihood methods in making the approximation.

The computer time required for each of these methods increases with the sophistication of the method used in obtaining the estimates, and often one is led to reduction techniques or approximations in applying the more sophisticated approaches in order to reduce the computer time.

The use of this approach in the analysis of a system or phenomena requires that the investigator has enough insight into and knowledge of his field to be able to formulate valid relationships among the variables to be studied. In the political and social sciences, he may thus be faced with a substantial problem of a degree of difficulty, since in these fields there is little available in the way of general guides. However, mathematical modelling of a system is more or less of an art, and the best one can do is to study the work done by others in related fields.

## VI. Response Surface Analysis

In 1951, Box and Wilson introduced a new concept into experimental design by recognizing that, in many situations, one is not so much interested in testing the significance of factors associated with a system, as simply to determine the best operating conditions for the system. The class of experimental designs introduced has become known as "response surface designs," and the associated analysis yielding the optimum operational conditions is known as "response surface analysis."

The behavior of any reaction is governed by laws which should be representable in mathematical form, and thus it should be possible to determine the optimum conditions for the reaction by simply applying these laws. However, one often finds in practice that the underlying mechanism of the system is so complicated that the mathematical representation using theoretical considerations is essentially impossible. This is particularly true in the social and political science fields. When one is faced with need to use the empirical approach and is interested in determining the best operating conditions, say, for an economic or political system, these response surface designs are appropriate.

The theory is developed assuming that the response, Y, is dependent upon n variables $X_i$, which are capable of measurement and control. The form of the functional relationship $Y = f(x_1, x_2, ..., x_n)$ is unknown, and the problem is to find the combination of values of $x_i$ which optimize the response within the region of the n-dimensional factor space where experimentation is feasible using as few experimental observations as possible. The number of observations required will, of course, depend upon the accuracy and precision of estimation desired. Where the problem is one of minimization, it can always be converted to one of maximization; for example, by considering the improvement as compared with some standard instead of the actual level achieved.

The technique assumes that the response function can be satisfactorily represented by a quadratic form in the area of interest, i.e.,

$$Y = \sum_i^n = 0 \sum_j^n \geqslant_i C_{ij} X_i X_j + e$$

where Y is the property to be maximized, the $\chi_i$ are the levels of the n independent variables ($\chi_0 = 1$), the $c_{ij}$ are the unknown parameters to be estimated from the experiment and e is the residual or experimental error. The adequacy of the quadratic surface representation of the true response surface of the process being investigated depends on the use of a small sub-region of the factor space within which one restricts his determinations. In some experimental situations, such a small neighborhood within which the optimum point can be assumed to lie is already known to the experimenter from previous experience. However, if this is not the case, the procedure of locating optimum conditions involves two distinct phases. The first phase involves the location of the neighborhood, while the second is to determine within the neighborhood the optimum point.

The location of the neighborhood is accomplished by using what is called the "method of steepest ascent." In this procedure, one assumes that the surface can be represented locally by a sloping plane. Starting at any point, P, the experimenter estimates the coefficients or slopes of the plane $Y = b_0 + b_1\chi_1 + b_2\chi_2 + \ldots b_n\chi_n$ by performing a suitably arranged set of trials in a small subregion about P. From these observations, the coefficients are estimated and one then calculates the direction of steepest ascent or greatest slope up the plane. He then proceeds to a point, Q, in this direction, where new observations are made, the slopes are redetermined, and the process repeated. In this way, by a step-by-step procedure, points of higher and higher response are reached.

This procedure cannot, however, be used actually to reach the maximum response point since, as one goes farther up the surface, the slopes become more gradual and thus more difficult to estimate. The second-order terms also become relatively more important. The procedure generally followed is to compare the linear effects with the error variance and with the second-order effects, and if the linear model appears adequate, the path of steepest ascent is determined. At the point of diminishing returns, the new point is located around which the process is repeated.

The experimental design used during the first phase where one is seeking the path of steepest ascent from a given point on the surface is generally of a two-level factorial type, where the origin for each variable is taken at the initial point and the levels used are equidistant from it in either direction. Thus, in a three- variable situation, one would use a $2^3$ factorial design, and the eight experimental points would be as shown in Table 1.

TABLE 1. Experimental Points for a $2^3$ Factorial Design

| Point | Factor Level | | |
|-------|:---:|:---:|:---:|
|       | $\chi_1$ | $\chi_2$ | $\chi_3$ |
| 1 | +1 | +1 | +1 |
| 2 | −1 | +1 | +1 |
| 3 | +1 | −1 | +1 |
| 4 | −1 | −1 | +1 |
| 5 | +1 | +1 | −1 |
| 6 | −1 | +1 | −1 |
| 7 | +1 | −1 | −1 |
| 8 | −1 | −1 | −1 |

The estimation of the b's from this type of design is straight-forward. In fact, if $\sigma^2$ is the experimental error variance, we have $b_i = \Sigma x_i y / \Sigma x_i^2$, and $V(b) = \sigma^2 / \Sigma x_i^2$ (the variance of b).

One thus has the essential ingredients needed to complete the first phase of the investigation.

In considering the second phase, we assume that we have identi-fied a point P that is in the neighborhood of the optimum point. The experimental designs used at this stage of the problem are known as composite designs. There are two types of composite designs, central and non-central. The central composite designs consider the $2^n$ factorial designs and adds additional points with high and low levels for each variable as well as additional points at the center of the design.

The central composite design for n=2 is shown in Figure 1. The $2^2$ factorial points are given as solid points while the added points are open circles.

FIGURE 1. A Two-Dimensional Central Composite Design

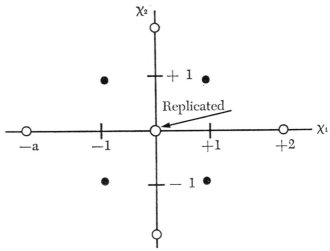

For the purpose of estimating the parameters of the quadratic form, the central composite design can be shown to be more effici-ent than the $3^n$ factorial dseign. As one might expect, this means that a saving in experimental points can be realized, since interest has been narrowed to estimating the optimum response point rather than to studying generally the nature of the mathematical model that explains the process under study.

The location of an optimum point usually requires a series of coordinated experiments, especially when one must first find the neighborhood of the optimum. If the process being studied has little or no time effect, so that one can combine results that are obtained at different time intervals, the series of experiments can often be developed into an organized sequential program. The non-central composite designs are useful if one uses such a sequential approach to his experimentation. The factorial portion and the central point are run first and, if the optimum is found to be close to the center being used in the factorial design, the additional points required for the central composite design are then used. If, however, the optimum response is nearer one of the other points the factorial portion is augmented to form a non-central composite design. Of course, if it is indicated that a new location should be sought through the use of the path of steepest ascent, then the sequence is as follows. The fitting of the quadratic surface, $Y = \sum_{i=0}^{n} \sum_{j \geq i}^{n} c_{ij} x_i x_j + e$, to the observations realized from the composite design can be obtained by standard multiple regression techniques. Following the estimation of the coefficients, one can perform an analysis of variance on the results to establish the significance of the several coefficients as well as the significance of the regression itself. If one has some prior information as to the value of $\sigma^2$, the experimental error, this information can be used in a comparison with the residual mean square associated with the regression analysis to provide a test of goodness of fit of the second-degree equation. If the fit is not satisfactory, one may change his neighborhood if this seems required, or increase the order of the regression equation.

When such a test has indicated that an adequate fit has been obtained, the fact that an individual coefficient is or is not statistically significant is of no practical significance. What this means is that one might just as well retain the small coefficient in his future analyses, since there appears to be no really good reason for making the hypothesis that one of the coefficients is actually zero in the population model.

When the second-degree equation has been fitted, it is necessary to interpret it to see if one can, in fact, determine the coordinates of the optimum response point. Since the coefficients in a general quadratic do not readily convey to the observer the nature of the surface being represented, one usually resorts to a canonical reduction of the equation so as to obtain the canonical form, $Y = b_0 + b_{11} \chi_1^2 + b_{22} \chi_2^2 + \dots b_{nn} \chi_n^2$.

There are many types of surfaces that can be obtained through the use of the quadratic function. Under certain conditions, including those where all the b's are negative, there will be a point maximum in all the variables. Another situation, however, that may be encountered is where the maximum is in fact remote from the region of the design, but the surface is elongated along an axis which passes close to the design. This indicates that the previous experimentation has brought the experimenter not to a maximum but close to a rising ridge of the surface. No conclusion as to optimum conditions can be drawn in this latter case, but one can, from observation of the nature of the rising ridge, determine where additional experimentation should be carried out in attempting to locate the optimum point. In the case that the optimum point falls within the region of the experiment, its position can be obtained by differentiating the original quadratic with respect to the variables $\chi_1, \chi_2, \ldots \chi_n$ in turn and equating the results to zero. This will yield a set of linear equations which, when solved simultaneously, give the coordinates of the optimum point. It should be emphasized, however, that the nature of the surface should be critically examined through the use of the canonical transformations approach before one seeks these coordinates. In fact, as the dimension of the problem increases, making a careful examination becomes most important.

The mechanics of analyzing the data obtained from the sequence of observations made in following the approach outlined above can be readily adapted to digital computer programs. In fact, many of the procedures make use of techniques for which standard computer programs are already generally available. Thus in the initial phase, where one is interested in following the path of steepest ascent using a linear fit to the experimental data, multiple regression computer programs are applicable. These programs give not only the best estimates for the regression coefficients but also their standard errors as well as the standard error of estimate for the response variable. Through the use of transformations, the significance of the quadratic terms in the surface can also be readily tested using the same computer program. This enables one to determine when to abandon the steepest ascent phase of the investigation.

In the calculation of the actual path of steepest ascent, the successive differentiation of the fitted linear relationship yields simultaneous linear equations whose solution can be obtained from standard programs for solving systems of simultaneous equations. In fact, even the determination of the possible steps up the path through the computation of coordinates of the points on the path can easily be programmed.

When one reaches the point of fitting the quadratic surface to the data obtained from a composite design, the determination of the coefficients of the surface, their standard errors and the standard error of estimate is also a multiple regression program application. The quadratic terms are simply treated as new linear variables in this case. The determination of the optimum point is again the solution of a set of simultaneous linear equations.

## VII. CLASSIFICATION TECHNIQUES

The theory of statistical classification deals with the problem of assigning one or more individuals to one of several possible groups or populations on the basis of a set of characteristics observed among them. Thus, the problem of classification can be considered as a special case or application of multi-variate decision theory. The nature of the observed characteristics may vary from problem to problem. In some cases they may be all of a measured type, while in another situation the variables may all be of the simple categorical type of attributes in which each observation can take on but one of a finite number of distinct values or states. Siegel has noted that "measurements may, in general, be from four scales: the nominal, ordinal, interval, and ratio scales. In any given multi-variate classification problem, the measurements may be of a mixture involving some or all of these types of variables." It should be expected that numerous approaches have been advanced as to how one should go about evolving a classification decision rule.

It should be recognized that since the area of interest has been designated as "statistical" classification, this means that the decision rule must be based upon observational data available from samples from the several populations rather than on known population characteristics. Thus we assume that we have a sample of individuals from each population and for each of these individuals we have available the same set of observations as are available for the individual requiring classification.

Consider for illustration a well-known classification problem, that of a prospective student applying for admission by submitting credentials such as his high school records and in addition being given a battery of admission tests. These data become the multivariate set of observations available on each applicant. The problem is to classify, in advance, the applicant into the population to which he belongs, where the alternatives are the population of those students who can successfully complete college training and the population of students who will not complete the college courses successfully. Available to the admissions office are the same data on former students, some known to have completed and the remaining known not to have completed college.

Let us now look at the steps required to evolve a classification rule. Statistical classification rules, in general, depend either upon the concept of likelihood where one considers the ratios of the likelihoods that the observation to be classified came from the suspect populations, or they depend upon the value of some classification statistic whose form is assumed and is evaluated for the individual requiring classification. The samples that are available from each population are used to estimate the likelihood ratios or the constants in the classification statistic, depending on which approach is being used.

There are four major steps that must be accomplished if one is to evolve a classification rule, in brief: selection of the variables, selection of the classification technique, selection of the decision rule, and an analysis of effectiveness. These we now consider.

*The Selection of the Variables to be Used in Making the Classification.*

Here one encounters problems such as whether or not to include in his observational vector variables of different types, how reliably each available variable can be measured or determined, the discrimination power of the variable relative to the populations of interest, the inter-relationship of the variables, and the cost of making each variable determination. The decisions of selection depend in the main on personal judgments, since at present no good selection rule exists.

*The Technique to be Used in Making the Classification Estimate and the Use of Available Sample Data to Make the Estimates.*

One can identify several estimation techniques in the literature; however, the best known technique for measured variables is to use the Wald Statistic, which is simply a linear function of the observations in the form

$$W(z) = \sum_{q=1}^{p} \sum_{p=1}^{p} \sigma^{pq} \left( \mu_q^{(2)} - \mu_q^{(1)} \right) z_p$$

where $\sigma^{pq} =$ general term in the inverse of the common covariance matrix and $\mu^{(i)}{}_q =$ mean of $\chi_q$ in population $\pi_i$.

*Selection of the Decision Rule to be Used in Making the Actual Classification Decision for a Given Observation.*

To discuss this step at this stage, it seems best to restrict our consideration to the two-population classification problem. We then have available for making the classification decision either a likelihood ratio that is a numerical function of the observational vector z, say, $L(z)$, or we have a classification statistic defined as a numerical function of z, say $C(z)$. In either case a decision rule is then simply the division of the $L(z)$ or $C(z)$ one-dimensional interval into two regions such that for those z's that yield an $L(z)$ or $C(z)$ that falls in region two, the individual will be classified into population two. Thus we have reduced the problem of classification to that of determining the region.

*Determining the Operational Effectiveness of the Classification Technique.*

Basic to the measurement of the operational effectiveness of any classification technique are the probabilities:

$p(i\backslash j) =$ the probability of misclassifying an individual who belongs in population $\pi_j$ into population $\pi_i$.

From these probabilities one can evolve expected cost estimates as well as other criteria of worth. To obtain estimates of these probabilities one requires the conditional distribution function of the likelihood ratios or the classification statistic used in the technique. In some cases these distributions can be expressed either exactly or approximately in mathematical form and then the misclassification probability estimations simply require the evaluation of an integral over the required region. When such a mathematical representation is not available, an empirical approach can be used involving the individual observations available in the samples to produce an empirical estimation of the conditional distributions. Here it seems best to discuss the details of this step around an actual problem.

For our problem let us assume that the admission office requires an admission policy such that the probability of a student's doing unsuccessful work if admitted should be less than or equal to one tenth.

1) *The Control of Error Approach.*

What is needed is the distribution function of the statistic $W(z)$

since we would like to select $\lambda$ such that $P[W(z) > \lambda \mid z$ belongs to $\pi_1] = 0.10$. We know that $W(z)$ is asymptotically normally distributed under the condition that $z$ belongs to $\pi_1$ with the mean,

$$\overline{W}_1 = \sum_{j=1}^{P} \sum_{i=1}^{P} \sigma ij \left( \mu_i^{(2)} - \mu_i^{(1)} \right) \mu_i^{(1)} \quad ,$$

and variance,

$$V_w = \sum_{j=1}^{P} \sum_{i=1}^{P} \sigma ij \left( \mu_j^{(2)} - \mu_j^{(1)} \right)\left( \mu_j^{(2)} - \mu_j^{(1)} \right).$$

For the sample data, we find upon substituting the appropriate sample characteristics into the formula for the means and variance that

$\overline{W}_1 = 7.746$   and
$V_w = 3.676$

Thus we have to solve for $\lambda$ in the equation

$$P(2 \mid 1) = \frac{1}{\sqrt{2\pi}} \int^{00}_{(\lambda - \overline{w}_1) / \sqrt{V_w}} e - z^2/^2 dz = 0.10.$$

From the table of areas under the normal curve we have

$$1.282 = \frac{\lambda - 7.746}{\sqrt{3.676}}$$

and
$\lambda = 10.20$
and our classification decision rule can be stated as:
"If $W(z) = + 0.0350z_1 + 0.0448z_2 + 0.12747z_3 > 10.20$ classify the observation as belonging to $\pi_2$."
(That is, admit the student to the curriculum.)

In a more general sense we can balance the two values of the two misclassification probabilities by selecting the appropriate value of $\lambda$ so as to meet any single constraint that might be imposed. For example, one may wish to control the errors such that two probabilities are equal. It is evident that the solution of the resulting integral equation may require a numerical technique of some sort.

2) *The Cost Control Approach.*

Consider in our student admission example that we have available the cost factors:

$C(2 \mid 1)$ = the cost of misclassifying an individual into population $\pi_2$ when he really belongs to $\pi_1$ (admitting a poor student) = 10 and

$C(1 \mid 2)$ = the cost of classifying an individual into population $\pi_1$ when he belongs to $\pi_2$ (failing to admit a good student) = 20.

$q_1$ = the a priori probability of a candidate for admission being from population $\pi_1$ = 0.25.

$q_2$ = the a priori probability of a candidate for admission being from population $\pi_2$ = 0.75.

Then if we wish an admission policy that would operate so as to minimize the expected loss, we have that

$L_\lambda = q_1 p(2 \mid 1,\lambda) c(2 \mid 1) + q_2 p(1 \mid 2,\lambda) c(1 \mid 2)$

where $L_\lambda$ is the expected loss. In our particular case,

$L_\lambda = (0.25)(10) p(2 \mid 1,\lambda) + (0.75)(20) p(1 \mid 2,\lambda) = 2.5 p(2 \mid 1,\lambda) + 15.0 p(1 \mid 2,\lambda)$.

So we seek a $\lambda$ which would minimize $L_\lambda$. One can simply try different values of $\lambda$, determine the $p(2 \mid 1, \lambda)$ and $p \mid 2,\lambda)$ corresponding to the $\lambda$ and then compute the $L_\lambda$. Since the relationship between $L_\lambda$ and $\lambda$ is quite smooth, one can through such a trial procedure approximate the appropriate minimizing value of $\lambda$ within three or four steps.

*Determining the Effectiveness of the Above Classification Rule.* In the case of the above two-populations—control of misclassification error situation—we compute the probabilities:

$P(2 \mid 1)$ − P (Admitting a student who subsequently does unsatisfactory work)

= P (Classifying z into $\pi_2$ when z belongs to $\pi_1$),

and

$P(1 \mid 2)$ = P (Failing to admit a student who could do successful work)

= P (Classifying z into $\pi_1$ when z belongs to $\pi_2$).

Under step 3 we determined the classification rule (i.e., the $\lambda$) such that $p(2 \mid 1) = 0.10$. To determine $p(1 \mid 2)$ we have

$$\overline{W_2} = \sum_{j=1}^{P} \sum_{i=1}^{P} \sigma_{ij} \left( \mu_j^{(2)} - \mu_j^{(1)} \right) \mu_i^{(2)} = 11.422,$$

and, due to the equal covariance assumption,

$V_w = 3.676$,

so,

$$P(1\,|\,2) = \frac{1}{\sqrt{2\pi}} \int_{-00}^{(10.20\,-\,11.422)\,/\,\sqrt{3.676}} e - z^2/^2 \, dz = 0.26.$$

The rationale in these probability evaluations can best be exhibited graphically (Figure 1).

FIGURE 1. Probability Evaluations

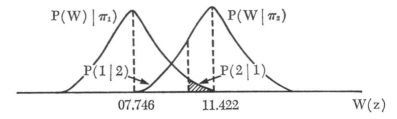

Thus we find that the operational effectiveness of the classification rule is such that $P(2\,|\,1) = 0.10$ and $P(1\,|\,2) = 0.26$. If one is disturbed over the size of $P(1\,|\,2)$, he can either increase the allowable size of $P(2\,|\,1)$ or he may seek additional or new variables that better discriminate between the two populations.

Essentially, each of the classification techniques identified above follows the four main development steps that were enumerated in detail for the Wald Classification Statistic. Two additional problems warrant special mention, however.

The first is the so-called distribution problem. That is, the requirement to have some knowledge as to how the statistic or likelihood ratio being used is distributed in probability under the condition that an individual comes from $\pi_2$. This knowledge is required if one wants to formulate the particular classification rule to meet an error control or cost criterion. It is also needed if one is to estimate measures of operational effectiveness. We used the information that $W(z)$ was normally distributed to generate these distribution requirements in the student admission illustrative example. One may, however, be interested in using a classification technique for which the mathematical form of its conditional probability distribution is unknown. In that case, especially if one has available a high speed digital computer and the sample sizes are sufficiently large, one can resort to the use of an empirically generated conditional distribution using the sample data. To illustrate the concept, let us suppose that we have available in the student admission problem data on 190 individuals known to be from population $\pi_1$ (unsuccessful). Then if the value of the statistic, $W_1(z)$ were computed for the 190 cases, these observations could be tabulated into a cumulated frequency distribution, the distribution plotted and a smooth distribution function drawn freehand to approximate the ogive of the underlying conditional probability distribution. From such graphical representation appropriate values of $P(2 \mid 1, \lambda)$ and $P(1 \mid 2, \lambda)$ could be determined for corresponding values of $\lambda$. In our error control classification rule for the college admission problem we would have the frequency distribution and graphical representation as shown in Table 1 and Figure 2.

TABLE 1. Frequency distribution for $W_1(z)$ college entrance problem, population $\pi_1(z)$

| Interval | Tally | Cum | % |
|---|---|---|---|
| 4.50 - 5.24 | 9 | 190 | 100 |
| 5.25 - 5.99 | 19 | 181 | 95 |
| 6.00 - 6.74 | 24 | 162 | 85 |
| 6.75 - 7.49 | 28 | 138 | 73 |
| 7.50 - 8.24 | 21 | 110 | 58 |
| 8.25 - 8.99 | 17 | 89 | 47 |
| 9.00 - 9.74 | 24 | 72 | 38 |
| 9.75 - 10.49 | 12 | 38 | 20 |
| 10.50 - 11.24 | 18 | 24 | 13 |
| 11.25 - 11.99 | 2 | 6 | 03 |
| 12.00 - 12.74 | 4 | 4 | 02 |

FIGURE 2. Empirical distribution of $W(z)$ given $\pi_1$

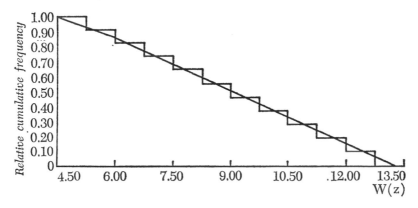

A comparable empirical estimate of the distribution of $W(z)$ under the condition that the observation belongs to population $\pi_2$ could be evolved through the use of the observation available in the sample from $\pi_2$. The only variation in the technique would be in the accumulation of the frequencies. In this second case one would accumulate the frequencies with increasing $W$'s.

Thus we would have an estimate of $P(2 \mid 1, \lambda)$ which yields the estimate of the probability of classifying an individual who is a $\pi_2$ as a $\pi_1$ if one used the decision rule "If $W(z) > \lambda$ classify the individual into $\pi_2$."

The second problem that warrants additional mention is the multi-population problem. Here we are interested in classification procedures that could classify an individual into one of the several populations, where the number of populations is greater than two.

If one can associate with each population, $\pi^i$, a $q_i$, the a priori probability of obtaining for classification an observation from population $\pi_i$, and a cost factor, $C(j \mid i)$, associated with mis-classifying an observation from $\pi_i$ as being from $\pi_j$, then a decision rule is available that will minimize the expected cost of making classification. The rule states that:
"If

$$\sum_{i=1, \neq k}^{p} q_i p_i(z) c(k \mid i) \qquad \sum_{i=1, \neq j}^{p} q_i p_i(z) c(j \mid i)$$

for all $j (j \neq k)$ then z should be classified into $\pi_k$."

If the inequality for some indices along with k, then it is immaterial as to whether the individual is classified into $\pi_k$ or one of the populations whose index yields the equality.

It should be noted that the practical use of these classification techniques will usually require the use of high speed computing facilities. This is especially true if the dimension of the problem is at all large or if one must empirically generate the conditional distribution of the statistic being used by utilizing the individual observations available in the samples. There are many unresolved problems associated with the use of many of these techniques, but it is felt that the systematic exploration of their applicability in many practical problems cannot help but advance the general state of the art. Although the discriminating power of the set of variables currently being accumulated can be determined, the characteristics of the underlying distributions and the relative effectiveness of the competitive procedures must in many respects be tackled pragmatically. Attention must be given to the problem of estimating both the underlying a priori probabilities associated with the populations being considered along with the misclassification cost factors. Individuals may feel that such refinements are inappropriate to their particular classification problem, but it can be argued that until one addresses himself to the problem in some such systematic and scientific way, no real improvement can be expected. The criterion of worth of any system is its operational effectiveness, and thus one should not only feel challenged to obtain estimates of the operational effectiveness of the "system" he is now using, but he should also investigate how the effectiveness may be improved by using one of the above statistical classification techniques.

### SELECTED BIBLIOGRAPHY

#### FACTOR ANALYSIS

COOLEY, W. W., and LOHNES, P. R. *Multivariate Procedures for the Behavioral Sciences.* New York: John Wiley & Sons, 1962.

HARMON, H. H. *Modern Factor Analysis.* Chicago: University of Chicago Press, 1962.

PITTS, F. R. *Urban Systems and Economic Development.* Eugene: University of Oregon Bureau of Business Research, 1962.

THURSTONE, L. L. *Multiple Factor Analysis.* Chicago: University of Chicago Press, 1947.

#### POWER SPECTRUM ANALYSIS

"Autocovariance and Power Spectral Analysis." Program No. BMDO2T, in W. J. DIXON (ed.), *BMD Biomedical Computer Programs.* Los Angeles: UCLA, 1964.

GRANGER, C. W. *Spectral Analysis of Economic Time Series.* Princeton: Princeton University Press, 1964.

ROSENBLATT, M. (ed.). *Proceedings of Symposium on Time Series Analysis.* New York: John Wiley & Sons, 1963.

#### CLUSTER ANALYSIS OR NUMERICAL TAXONOMY

COOLEY, W. W., and LOHNES, P. R. *Multivariate Procedures for the Behavioral Sciences.* New York: John Wiley & Sons, 1962 (chap. vi).

SOKAL, R. P., and SNEATH, P. H. A. *The Principles of Numerical Taxonomy.* San Francisco and London: W. H. Freeman & Co., 1963.

TANAMOTO, T. T. *IBM Taxonomy Application.* New York: IBM Data Processing Division, 1961.

#### GENERAL LINEAR HYPOTHESIS

BARGMANN, R. E. "A Statistician's Instructions to the Computer: A Report on a Statistical Computer Language," in *Proceedings of the IBM Scientific Computing Symposium on Statistics.* New York, 1963.

"General Linear Hypothesis." Program No. BMDO5U, in W. J. DIXON (ed.), *BMD Biomedical Computer Programs.* Los Angeles: UCLA, 1964.

GRAYBILL, F. A. *An Introduction to Linear Statistical Models.* New York: McGraw-Hill, 1961.

POSTEN, H. O. "Analysis of Variance & Analysis of Regression with More Than One Response," in *Application of Statistics and Computers to Fuel and Lubricant Research Problems.* San Antonio: SW Research Institute, 1962.

SIMULTANEOUS LINEAR REGRESSION

EISENPRESS, H. *Forecasting by Econometric Systems.* New York: IBM Data Processing Division, 1962.

GIRSHICK, M. A., and HAAVELMO, T. "Statistical Analysis of the Demand for Food: Examples of Simultaneous Estimation of Structural Equations," *Econometrica,* XV (1947), 79-110.

HAAVELMO, T. "The Statistical Implications of a System of Simultaneous Equations," *Econometrica,* XI (1943), 1-12.

KLEIN, L. R. *A Textbook of Econometrics.* Evanston: Row, Peterson & Co., 1953.

RESPONSE SURFACE ANALYSIS

BOX, G. E. P. "The Exploration and Exploitation of Response Surfaces: Some General Considerations and Examples," *Biometrics,* X (1954), 16-60.

————, and WILSON, K. B. "On the Experimental Attainment of Optimum Conditions," *Journal of the Royal Statistical Society,* Series B, XIII (1951), 1-45.

DAVIES, O. L. *Design and Analysis of Industrial Experiments.* New York: Hofner Pub. Co., 1956.

CLASSIFICATION TECHNIQUES

ANDERSON, T. W. "Classification by Multivariate Analysis," *Psychometrika,* XVI (1951), 31-50.

————. *An Introduction to Multivariate Statistical Analysis.* New York: John Wiley & Sons, 1958 (chap. vi).

KOSSACK, C. F. *A Handbook on Classification.* LaFayette: Purdue University Research Publication, 1962.

WALD, A. "On the Statistical Problem Arising in the Classification of an Individual into One of Two Groups," *Annals of Mathematical Statistics,* XV (1944), 145-62.

# 3. Applications to Practical Politics

# 3. Applications to Practical Politics

## Introductory Note

*The good Christian should beware of mathematicians . . .*
*—St. Augustine*

*O brave new world, that has such people in't!*
*—Shakespeare*

Andrew Hacker has suggested that the use of electromagnetic computers to simulate the political behavior of the real world has led to essentially trivial findings. A major fault, he notes, is that these enterprises are committee operations. "Computers . . . have no judgment. The sad thing is that those who are running the machines are themselves reluctant to exercise that quality which the computer lacks. One reason is that most such projects are team operations."[1] Hacker's example of this kind of futile activity is the attempt to simulate voter reaction in the 1960 presidential primary in Wisconsin.

By coincidence the 1960 Wisconsin primary model is the subject of the first part of the article by Frank Scalora in this volume. This model has been criticized also on the ground that the procedure permits a sinister manipulation of voter information, and leads to thought control and to "brainwashing." This view has been expressed by some prominent American political leaders, and it is consistent with the point of view of those traditionalist political philosophers who emphasize ethical and normative approaches. Evaluation of the Wisconsin model based on this frame of reference is obviously in sharp contrast with that of Hacker, for it suggests that the model is important and deserves careful and critical attention.

The Scalora paper deals with problems in politics and advertising. The model is designed to aid a candidate by furnishing insights which can be used to persuade voters to support him, and it is designed to aid a firm in persuading university graduates to go to work for it. The important question is whether the model achieves an efficient solution to these problems. If its value is negligible, it will not be because it is the product of a committee and utilizes a computer.

---

[1] "Mathematics and Political Science," in James C. Charlesworth (ed.), *Mathematics and the Social Sciences* (Philadelphia: American Academy of Political and Social Sciences, 1963), pp. 65-69.

The Scalora model offers enhanced efficiency to those who want to manipulate human behavior. Its successful employment is a legitimate subject of concern in normative terms, as well as proof that Hacker was in error to dismiss it lightly. The history of science is full of evidence that solutions to old problems often create new problems. This is an inevitable consequence of change. The progress of science and social change point toward complexity, not toward doomsday or the heavenly city.

The article by Gerald Kramer is, like that of Scalora, designed to solve a problem of so-called practical politics. The aim of the model is the optimum allocation of scarce resources in a pre-election canvass. Output is measured in terms of votes won, or of votes gained. The political problem is, therefore, closely analogous to the resource allocation problems common to economics. Yet the fact that it is political is a source of specific difficulties. Votes won, or votes gained, are a difficult commodity to measure. The author, qualified in both mathematics and political science, has produced an imaginative model. If he solves the canvassing problem, other resource allocation activities, such as television advertising, may become amenable to model solutions that are not presently available.

These models may be of little interest to the student of systems analysis or grand theory. Scalora and Kramer are concerned with relatively modest problems compared with war and peace, survival in the nuclear age, the pursuit of justice, or the proper construction of nation-states. In a sense the aims of these papers are prediction and control, rather than understanding and extension of basic knowledge, and consequently the models may be less useful to political scholars than to the practitioners of the art of winning elections. On the other hand, as Havelock Ellis has observed: "In philosophy, it is not the attainment of the goal that matters, it is the things that are met with by the way." If one appraises the work of political scientists in the light of the widely differing perceptions of what ought to be done,[2] it is evident that there is work aplenty for all. Some may devote themselves to great tasks, while others perform tasks which are immediately useful.

[2] See, for example, Charles S. Hyneman, *The Study of Politics: The Present State of American Political Science* (Urbana: University of Illinois Press, 1959) and Albert Somit and Joseph Tanenhaus, *American Political Science: A Profile of a Discipline* (New York: Atherton Press, 1964).

# Stochastic Models in the Behavorial Sciences: Applications to Elections and Advertising

FRANK S. SCALORA

*IBM—World Trade Corporation*

The use of mathematics in the behavioral sciences has benefited from the availability of modern computing machines. It is now possible to take a behavioral situation, put it into a mathematical framework which simulates it, and then try it out on the machine. If good data are available the validity of the mathematical model can be tested and then simulation runs made, increasing our understanding of the behavioral situation. It would be unrealistic to attempt to do this by hand because of the difficulties both of handling of data and of time availability.

We shall discuss in this paper a common type of behavioral situation and the mathematical models developed to describe two applications. The situation is basically that of an election, although it can be interpreted in many ways.

In a political campaign, each candidate must decide which issues to stress to help him win over his opponent. The advertising campaign for a product consists of telling the consumer about its especially good qualities to the detriment of competing products. The recruiting manager of a company has to find out what are the most effective aspects to stress in a campaign to get the best people for the job.

All of these situations involve a population and competitors who are trying to influence the population by communicating with them. We will now describe the way these situations can be put into a useful mathematical framework. The problem would have remained intractable but for the availability of computing machines to store and process huge quantities of data at high speeds and the uniting of sociological and mathematical ideas.

The election model discussed here was developed by a research group at IBM, of which the author was a member together with Dr. William N. McPhee. Dr. McPhee has reported on the results obtained when the model was used in the 1960 Wisconsin Primary in McPhee: *Formal Theories of Mass Behavior* (London: Free Press of Glencoe, 1963). The college recruitment model was developed by the author of SBC with the consulting help of Dr. McPhee. Earlier reports on the work have appeared in the Proceedings, Eighth Annual Convention, New York, Advertising Research Foundation, Fall, 1962 and Robert D. Buzzell; *Mathematical Models and Marketing Management* (Boston: Division of Research, Harvard Business School, Boston, 1964).

In simulating a situation of the kind discussed here, we must isolate the main forces which are at work and describe them mathematically. Thus, we have a population which is being asked to make a choice among various competitors as the competitors address messages or communications to them. We think of the individual member of the population as a person with preconceived ideas about the competitors which are, however, undergoing changes because of external forces generated by the campaigns of the competitors and environmental forces caused by the people with whom he associates. The model measures the change in a person's initial evaluations of the competitors in the course of the campaign. We will later discuss the results obtained when the model was applied on the simulation of a recruiting campaign.

The population is represented in the computer by a replica, a representative sample of it. On the basis of answers to a questionnaire, large quantities of information about the sample are stored in the machine. To keep the setting completely general, we will continue to use the terms population and competitors. The reader can easily translate these terms to electorate and candidates, in the case of an election campaign; consumers and brands of products, in the case of a consumer product advertising campaign; students and companies, in the case of company recruiting campaigns involving college students. The reader should have little difficulty in thinking of other situations close to his own experience which are describable in terms of the model.

The model formalizes the above observations. It consists of three processes or phases which abstract the preceding remarks. We begin with a representative sample of the population. The sample is stratified into homogeneous sub-samples dependent upon the application in question. For example, an election grouping might be a socio-economic or religious-ethnic one. A consumer grouping might be socio-economic or some other grouping which delineates among buying patterns. A college recruiting grouping might be on lines of major field and career interest, etc.

It is supposed that at the beginning each person in the sample has given an overall rating of each of the competitors, say on a scale of one-to-ten, although the scale may change from application to application. These ratings may be obtained directly from responses to a questionnaire as was done in the recruiting study previously mentioned, or indirectly through a Lazarsfeld latent structure analysis as was done in the election model, or possibly in other ways. Each competitor will then try to increase the person's evaluation of itself relative to its competitors. In real life, the competitors will try to accomplish this by advertising or stressing themes which they feel are particularly favorable to them. The model simulates this by what we call a stimulation process.

In the stimulation process, we pick a theme or issue for each competitor to stress. With Thurstone, we interpret a theme or stimulus as a probability distribution. Thus, a candidate's statement on civil rights will affect Negroes somewhat differently from White Liberals and much differently from White Southern Conservatives. A company's stressing of its pre-eminence in the computing business will cause different reactions among students interested in computers and students interested in pure mathematical research. Thus, the effect of a stimulus will vary depending on the group to which the person belongs. In fact, for each group we have computed probability tables which relate overall ratings of the competitors with ratings on the given theme or issue. Then the response of a person to a stimulus is obtained through a random process depending on the probability distribution peculiar to the person's group. We illustrate this by exhibiting a simplified "stimulus" table, which came up in our recruiting study. This table represents the theme (Issue 8), "Encouragement of Ingenuity" for Company A for a group of engineering students interested in physics.

### Response to Issue 8 for Company A

|  |  | Very High | High | Moderate | Low | Very Low |
|---|---|---|---|---|---|---|
| *Overall Rating* | Very High | .55 | .45 | — | — | — |
|  | High | .33 | .59 | .08 | — | — |
|  | Moderate | .20 | .60 | .20 | — | — |
|  | Low | — | .58 | .42 | — | — |
|  | Very Low | — | — | — | 1.00 | — |

We obtained these numbers by the use of a mathematical formula on the basis of answers to specific questions in the questionnaire. There are, however, other ways of doing this. The model interprets this table as follows: if a person in the group has given Company A a very high overall rating, then we can expect him to give a very high response to Company A's use of Issue 8 (Encouragement of Ingenuity) 55 per cent of the time and a high response 45 per cent of the time. If he gives Company A a high overall rating, then he can be expected to respond very highly to the use of this issue 33 per cent of the time, highly 59 per cent of the time, and moderately 8 per cent of the time, etc. Thus, we allow the person to make a temporary response to the themes communicated by the competitors by the use of these tables through a Monte Carlo technique.

At this point, we assume that a person will want to check his responses. Here we borrow an idea due to K. Lewin. In real life, a person can check certain statements directly. For example, he can check the fact that a glass can be broken with a hammer by actually hitting a piece of glass with a hammer. In the situation which we are discussing, however, he will not be able to check so easily. For example, he cannot check objectively the statement that one company is better to work for than another without actually working for both, or that Governor Romney will make a good President, etc. The next best approach is for him to compare his feelings with those of a friend. The model handles this by what we call "the discussion process." We pick a friend for the person from his group. If the friend confirms his impressions, then we assume that the person's temporary responses to the stimuli to which he has been exposed are now permanent and are ready to become part of his experience. If the friend does not confirm his impressions, he will not necessarily accept his friend's impressions over his own, but will want to rethink the situation. The model approximates this by exposing him to the same stimuli as before. We now accept his emerging responses as permanent.

Finally, we assume that the person will incorporate his surviving responses into his experience. In real life situations, the person is making new evaluations based on past preferences and new stimuli in a subjective fashion. The model accomplishes this by what we call a "learning process." The learning process consists of a formula which computes new overall evaluations of the competitors for the person involved. The formula "averages" the person's initial overall evaluations with the surviving responses emerging from the stimulation and discussion processes, subject to the quantity of knowledge that the person thinks he has about the competitors. We have previously computed these knowledgability numbers for each person. One thing implicit in the formula is that a person who thinks he knows a lot about the competitors will be harder to change than one who thinks he knows less.

We have actually described one stage, or cycle, of the model. We then store information about how the members of the sample

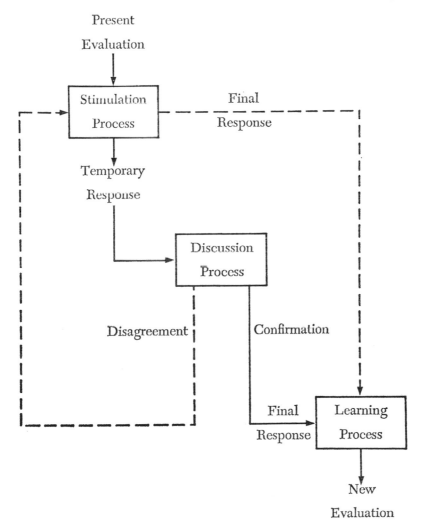

respond to the themes or issues which are likely to be used by the competitors in their campaigns. At the end of a cycle, the person may be exposed to new stimuli by the competitors. Now, however, he will go into the stimulation process with new overall evaluations. A glance at the simplified stimulus table shown above illustrates a point which we now make.

Subsequent communications by the competitors build on the changes in a person's attitude. Specifically, the learning process causes slow changes in the overall ratings in the specific direction toward the rating of the competitor on the specific issue being stressed. This improvement, or deterioration, is a double process because as his overall rating improves, say from high to very high, then he is more likely to get a very high response to the stimulus than he was before. Then, in turn, that will make him improve his overall rating still further. Alternatively, as his overall rating decreases, say from very high to high, then his distribution of probabilities is worse. He will be less likely to get a "very high" response than before, and may get some "moderate" responses, also. This will make his overall rating deteriorate still further.

We illustrate the above remarks by the flow chart of the model (see p. 115). It describes one cycle of the model.

*The Election Model*

We now give the essential details of the election model. We will not discuss any of its implications since these have been described in W. N. McPhee: *Formal Theories of Mass Behavior* (London: The Free Press of Glencoe, 1963). The references here are to the Wisconsin presidential primary in 1960.

A. *Input*
   1. The Voters

A sample of 1,783 Wisconsin voters was considered. The voters can be grouped in several ways. We give a possible grouping along religious-ethnic lines.

| Group Number | Description | Number of Voters |
|---|---|---|
| 1 | German Catholic Urban | 176 |
| 2 | German Catholic Rural | 124 |
| 3 | German Lutheran Urban | 169 |
| 4 | German Lutheran Rural | 134 |
| 5 | German Unaffiliated Urban | 76 |
| 6 | German Unaffiliated Rural | 65 |
| 7 | Great Britain Protestant | 122 |

| 8  | Great Britain Unaffiliated       | 61    |
|----|----------------------------------|-------|
| 9  | Scandinavian Urban               | 77    |
| 10 | Scandinavian Rural               | 106   |
| 11 | Polish Urban                     | 82    |
| 12 | Polish Rural                     | 27    |
| 13 | Irish Catholic                   | 58    |
| 14 | Other Eastern European Urban     | 78    |
| 15 | Other Eastern European Rural     | 54    |
| 16 | Other Western European Urban     | 42    |
| 17 | Other Western European Rural     | 34    |
| 18 | Other                            | 298   |
|    |                                  | 1,783 |

In addition the voters are broken down by congressional districts, of which there are ten in all.

Each voter is given a complex of numbers at the beginning: INT, $P_H$, $P_K$, $P_R$, $\Sigma H$, $\Sigma K$, $\Sigma R$, $\Sigma N$, C, $C_{i-1}$, G, FRD. Definitions of these numbers follow:

INT : A number designating the strength of the voter's interest in his candidate of preference at the time in question (empty at beginning).

$P_H$ : The voter's partisanship number (overall rating) for the candidacy of Senator Humphrey.

$P_K$ : The voter's partisanship number (overall rating) for the candidacy of Senator Kennedy.

$P_R$ : The voter's partisanship number (overall rating) for the candidacy of Vice President Nixon.

These three numbers were obtained originally through a process called "latent structure analysis." They are non-negative and are bounded by 05 and 95 except at the beginning.

$\Sigma H$ : A non-negative number reflecting the voter's cumulative involvement with the candidacy of Senator Humphrey.

$\Sigma K$ : A non-negative number reflecting the voter's cumulative involvement with the candidacy of Senator Kennedy.

$\Sigma R$ : A non-negative number reflecting the voter's cumulative involvement with the candidacy of Vice President Nixon.

$\Sigma N$ : A non-negative number reflecting the voter's cumulative involvement with no party.

These four numbers are obtained from the partisanship numbers and a number $M_v$ for each voter which is determined according to the answer to certain poll questions.

C      :      The voter's choice of candidate at the time in question (empty at beginning).

$\quad\quad\quad\quad$ C = 1.   Choice for Humphrey
$\quad\quad\quad\quad\quad\quad$ 2.   Choice for Kennedy
$\quad\quad\quad\quad\quad\quad$ 3.   Choice for Nixon
$\quad\quad\quad\quad\quad\quad$ 4.   Non-Voting Choice

$C_{i\text{-}1}$    :      The voter's previous choice.

G      :      The voter's group number, e.g., $1 \leqslant G \leqslant 18$ for the grouping which we have listed.

FRD   :      The address in storage of another voter who is referred to as the voter's friend with whom he presumably discusses the election.

### 2. The Stimulus Tables

The voters will be subjected to certain stimuli which are primarily the key election issues. Given a candidate and a group of voters, a stimulus table is developed for each stimulus. The table ranks the stimulus according to intensity: 20 (very weak), 40 (weak), 60 (neutral), 80 (strong), 100 (very strong), and probability intervals going from 00 to 99.

The stimulus table is merely a convenient way of assigning one of these intensity (stimulus) numbers to a voter with a certain probability. The probability that a particular number is chosen is determined by the length of its corresponding probability interval. To illustrate, consider the following table:

| Intensity | Corresponding Probability Interval |
|:---------:|:----------------------------------:|
| 20 | 00 - 09 |
| 40 | 10 - 24 |
| 60 | 25 - 44 |
| 80 | 45 - 69 |
| 100 | 70 - 99 |

According to what was just said a voter with the above table will be assigned intensity number 20 with probability .10 $(09 - 00 + 1)$; 40 with .15 $(24 - 10 + 01)$; 60 with .20 $(44 - 25 + 01)$; 80 with .25 $(69 - 45 + 01)$; and 100 with .30 $(99 - 70 + 01)$.

Two sets of simulus tables were constructed, three person tables and two person tables. The use of the three person stimulus tables presupposes that each candidate wages a full campaign. Since this was not the case in Wisconsin, where Nixon did not campaign, we were led to construct two person stimulus tables for Humphrey and Kennedy and special tables for Nixon. The special tables for Nixon reflect one of three levels of campaigning—Normal Campaigning, Moderate Campaigning, and No Campaigning.

B.  *Working of the Model*

The input is now subjected to three processes.

1.  The Stimulation Process

Given a stimulus for each candidate, we subject a given voter to it in the following way: Three random numbers $RN_H$, $RN_K$, $RN_R$ (between 00 and 99) are chosen which determine the intervals in the appropriate stimulus tables, and thus uniquely determine stimulus numbers $STIM_H$, $STIM_K$, $STIM_R$ ( $=20, 40, 60, 80$, or $100$).

The voter has already given to him partisanship numbers $P_H$, $P_K$, $P_R$. We compute:

$$INT_H = P_H + STIM_H$$
$$INT_K = P_K + STIM_K$$
$$INT_R = P_R + STIM_R$$

If the two largest INT's are equal then we call the result a tie and go through the same process again until there are no ties. At this point, the largest INT is called $INT_{max}$. There is a number called $INT_{min}=100$ with which $INT_{max}$ is compared. If $INT_{max} <$ $INT_{min}=100$ then $C=4$, i.e., the voter is a non-voter (the machine puts 4 into the C position and $INT_{max}$ into the INT position). Otherwise, $C=1, 2$, or $3$ according as $INT_H$, $INT_K$, or $INT_R$ is $INT_{max}$, and $INT_{max}$ becomes the new INT.

2.  The Discussion Process

Each voter has assigned to him a friend randomly. A given voter V comes into the discussion process with interest and choice numbers $INT_V$, $C_V$ from the stimulation stage. Similarly, the friend has numbers $INT_F$, $C_F$. If $INT_V + INT_F \geq MINM=200$ (minimum joint interest) then we say that discussion takes place. Otherwise, no discussion takes place, and both voter and friend are unchanged and are returned to storage, the voter voting according to $INT_V$

and $C_V$. When discussion takes place we compare $C_V$ and $C_F$. If:

(1)   $C_V = C_F$ then the voter and his friend are unchanged.

(2)   $C_V = 1$ or 2 and $C_F = 3$ or vice versa, then again the voter and his friend are unchanged.

(3)   $C_V = 1$, 2, or 3 and $C_F = 4$ or vice versa then the non-voter is sent back through the stimulation process.

(4)   $C_V = 1$ and $C_F = 2$ or vice versa then both voter and friend are sent back through the stimulation process, but only through Humphrey and Kennedy stimulus tables.

When every voter has been subjected to the discussion process he has final choice and interest numbers, and final C's are counted up to give the vote. It is possible to take the discussion process out of the model and proceed to the next stage, the learning process.

### 3.  The Learning Process

Every voter enters this stage with the numbers INT, C, $\Sigma H$, $\Sigma K$, $\Sigma R$, $\Sigma N$ with the first two having come from the preceding stage. If $C = 4$, $100 - \text{INT}$ is added to $\Sigma N$ to get the new $\Sigma N$ and the other $\Sigma$'s remain unchanged.

If $C = 1$, 2, or 3 then $\text{INT} - 100$ is added respectively to $\Sigma H$, $\Sigma K$, or $\Sigma R$ to get the new $\Sigma H$, $\Sigma K$, or $\Sigma R$ and the other $\Sigma$'s remain unchanged. We then compute new partisanship numbers as follows:

$$P_H = \frac{\Sigma H}{\Sigma H + \Sigma K + \Sigma R + \Sigma N}$$

$$P_K = \frac{\Sigma K}{\Sigma H + \Sigma K + \Sigma R + \Sigma N}$$

$$P_R = \frac{\Sigma R}{\Sigma H + \Sigma K + \Sigma R + \Sigma N}$$

These numbers are then rounded off so that they stay in the range between 05 and 95. Thus if $P_H > 95$ it is changed to 95 and if $0 < P_H < 05$ it is changed to 05. These three numbers then become the new partisanship numbers for the voter and he is ready to be subjected to a new set of stimuli.

### C.  Output

The basic output consists of the following:

1. The names of the candidates followed by the stimuli that they are using to stimulate the electorate at the point in question.

### 2. *Election Intentions*

This is a tabulation of the voting after the stimulation process. It includes the names of the candidates together with their vote totals and the no-vote totals, the corresponding percentages, and the percentages based on the actual number of people who have voted. This is then followed by the voting subtotals by groups. Example:

*Election Intentions*

|  | Total | Percent | Percent Voting |
|---|---|---|---|
| Humphrey | 354 | 20 | 31 |
| Kennedy | 412 | 23 | 36 |
| Nixon | 392 | 22 | 34 |
| No Vote | 625 | 35 | |
| Total: | 1,783 | | |

*Subtotals by Groups*

1   2   3   4   5   6   7   8   9   10   11   12   13   14   15   16   17   18

Humphrey

13   10   36   35   24   18   35   15   15   29   12   2   2   12   10   11   6   69

Kennedy

69   58   20   20   9   15   6   9   18   9   32   11   36   28   13   7   5   47

Nixon

37   13   42   27   22   9   43   17   17   29   5   3   6   15   4   5   4   94

No Vote

57   43   71   52   21   23   38   20   27   39   33   11   14   23   27   19   19   88

### 3. *Election Results*

This is a tabulation of the voting after the discussion process. Of course, if the discussion process is removed, then this appears after the stimulation process and replaces the Election Intentions.

### 4. *Election Results by Congressional Districts*

This is a tabulation of the election results percentages by congressional districts. An example follows:

| Congressional Districts | Percent Humphrey | Percent Kennedy | Percent Nixon |
|---|---|---|---|
| 1 | 31 | 33 | 36 |
| 2 | 29 | 37 | 34 |
| 3 | 33 | 32 | 35 |
| 4 | 28 | 39 | 33 |
| 5 | 29 | 34 | 37 |
| 6 | 29 | 37 | 34 |
| 7 | 32 | 35 | 33 |
| 8 | 29 | 42 | 29 |
| 9 | 35 | 29 | 36 |
| 10 | 33 | 35 | 32 |

## 5. Election Results by Groups

This is a tabulation of the election vote percentages by groups. Example:

| Group | Percent Humphrey | Percent Kennedy | Percent Nixon |
|---|---|---|---|
| 1. German Catholic Urban | 11 | 58 | 31 |
| 2. German Catholic Rural | 12 | 72 | 16 |
| 3. German Lutheran Urban | 37 | 20 | 43 |
| 4. German Lutheran Rural | 43 | 24 | 33 |
| 5. German Unaffiliated Urban | 44 | 16 | 40 |
| 6. German Unaffiliated Rural | 43 | 36 | 21 |
| 7. Great Britain Protestant | 42 | 7 | 51 |
| 8. Great Britain Unaffiliated | 37 | 22 | 41 |
| 9. Scandinavian Urban | 30 | 36 | 34 |
| 10. Scandinavian Rural | 43 | 13 | 44 |
| 11. Polish Urban | 24 | 65 | 11 |
| 12. Polish Rural | 13 | 69 | 18 |
| 13. Irish Catholic | 5 | 82 | 13 |
| 14. Other Eastern European Urban | 22 | 51 | 27 |
| 15. Other Eastern European Rural | 37 | 48 | 15 |
| 16. Other Western European Urban | 48 | 30 | 22 |
| 17. Other Western European Rural | 40 | 33 | 27 |
| 18. Other | 33 | 22 | 45 |

*The College Recruiting Model*

We now discuss the College Recruiting Model, some details of which have appeared in R. D. Buzzell: *Mathematical Models and Marketing Management* (Boston: Division of Research, Harvard Business School, 1964).

The problem we considered was one in which four companies were seeking the services of honor students majoring in engineering, mathematics, and physics. An earlier study had shown that in evaluating a company as a place to work, such students considered twelve issues to be particularly critical. These issues are:

1. The company's standing in your major field of career interest.
2. The caliber of its personnel.
3. The opportunities it provides to do challenging work.
4. The opportunities it provides for rapid advancement.
5. The quality of its products or services.
6. How hard the company drives to achieve its goals.
7. Its special training program . . . formal courses offered, etc.
8. The encouragement it gives individuals to use their own ingenuity in tackling problems.
9. The amount of basic research the company undertakes.
10. The extent to which the company is considerate of employees while striving for maximum profits.
11. Starting salary.
12. The amount of financial aid and other assistance it gives to help employees obtain advanced degrees.

These twelve issues then became the stimuli to be used in the stimulation process in the model, the themes which the companies would be expected to use in their advertising.

A sample of honor students majoring in engineering mathematics and physics from five universities was obtained and polled in January and again in May, 1961, at the close of the school year.[*] In addition, separate samples drawn from the same population were quizzed at intervals within this period to determine which communications were getting across. The samples were then divided into mutually exclusive sub-samples according to career interest.

---

[*] The selection and polling of the samples was done by Benton & Bowles.

A sample of about 250 students was considered. After rejection of some inadequate questionnaires, the students were grouped in the following way:

| Group Number | Description | No. of Students |
|---|---|---|
| 1 | Engineering students interested in computers | 39 |
| 2 | Engineering students interested in physics | 49 |
| 3 | Engineering students interested in systems | 49 |
| 4 | Engineering students interested in general engineering | 23 |
| 5 | Mathematics, physics students interested in computers | 23 |
| 6 | Mathematics, physics students interested in mathematics | 22 |
| 7 | Mathematics, physics students interested in physics | 29 |
| | | 234 |

The students were asked to give an overall evaluation of each of the four companies as a place to work, and also an evaluation on each of the twelve issues. A scale of one to ten was used for each rating. On the basis of this information, we were able to compute the stimulus tables described below.

Each student is represented by a vector of numbers. Here the subscript indicates the time stage of the game, and the superscript the company involved.

$$I_n, I_n^{(j)}, 1 \leqslant j \leqslant 4; P_n^{(j)}, 1 \leqslant j \leqslant 4; K^{(j)}, 1 \leqslant j \leqslant 4; \Sigma_n^{(j)}, 1 \leqslant j \leqslant 4; C; G; F.$$

At the beginning, $n = 0$ and $I_o, I_o^{(j)}$ are empty.

$P_o^{(j)}$ : The initial partisanship number (overall rating) for the jth company, is the student's own rating of the jth company as a place to work. It is an integer between 1 and 10, and was obtained from a questionnaire.

$K^{(j)}$ : An integer between 1 and 4 indicating how fixed the student's attitude toward the jth company is. A high $K^{(j)}$ indicates the student will be more difficult to influence than one with a low $K^{(j)}$.

$\Sigma_o^{(j)}$ : Given by the formula $\Sigma_o^{(j)} = K^{(j)} P_o^{(j)}$.

C : The choice number. An integer from 1 to 4 indicating after each cycle or stage, the company the student would be most likely to choose if he were forced to make a choice then.

G    :    The group number. An integer from 1 to 7 indicating to which group the student belongs.

F    :    The address of a friend in storage.

In addition, each student is labeled as to whether a given stimulus is not so important, somewhat important, or very important to him.

Given a company and a group of students, a stimulus table was developed for each stimulus. The stimulus table takes the following form:

| | | 10 | 9 | 8 | 7 | 6 | 5 | 4 | 3 | 2 | 1 |
|---|---|---|---|---|---|---|---|---|---|---|---|
| Overall Rating of the Company as a Place to Work | 10 | $p_{10,10}$ | $p_{10,9}$ | $p_{10,8}$ | $p_{10,7}$ | $p_{10,6}$ | $p_{10,5}$ | $p_{10,4}$ | $p_{10,3}$ | $p_{10,2}$ | $p_{10,1}$ |
| | 9 | $p_{9,10}$ | $p_{9,9}$ | $p_{9,8}$ | $p_{9,7}$ | $p_{9,6}$ | $p_{9,5}$ | $p_{9,4}$ | $p_{9,3}$ | $p_{9,2}$ | $p_{9,1}$ |
| | 8 | $p_{8,10}$ | $p_{8,9}$ | $p_{8,8}$ | $p_{8,7}$ | $p_{8,6}$ | $p_{8,5}$ | $p_{8,4}$ | $p_{8,3}$ | $p_{8,2}$ | $p_{8,1}$ |
| | 7 | $p_{7,10}$ | $p_{7,9}$ | $p_{7,8}$ | $p_{7,7}$ | $p_{7,6}$ | $p_{7,5}$ | $p_{7,4}$ | $p_{7,3}$ | $p_{7,2}$ | $p_{7,1}$ |
| | 6 | $p_{6,10}$ | $p_{6,9}$ | $p_{6,8}$ | $p_{6,7}$ | $p_{6,6}$ | $p_{6,5}$ | $p_{6,4}$ | $p_{6,3}$ | $p_{6,2}$ | $p_{6,1}$ |
| | 5 | $p_{5,10}$ | $p_{5,9}$ | $p_{5,8}$ | $p_{5,7}$ | $p_{5,6}$ | $p_{5,5}$ | $p_{5,4}$ | $p_{5,3}$ | $p_{5,2}$ | $p_{5,1}$ |
| | 4 | $p_{4,10}$ | $p_{4,9}$ | $p_{4,8}$ | $p_{4,7}$ | $p_{4,6}$ | $p_{4,5}$ | $p_{4,4}$ | $p_{4,3}$ | $p_{4,2}$ | $p_{4,1}$ |
| | 3 | $p_{3,10}$ | $p_{3,9}$ | $p_{3,8}$ | $p_{3,7}$ | $p_{3,6}$ | $p_{3,5}$ | $p_{3,4}$ | $p_{3,3}$ | $p_{3,2}$ | $p_{3,1}$ |
| | 2 | $p_{2,10}$ | $p_{2,9}$ | $p_{2,8}$ | $p_{2,7}$ | $p_{2,6}$ | $p_{2,5}$ | $p_{2,4}$ | $p_{2,3}$ | $p_{2,2}$ | $p_{2,1}$ |
| | 1 | $p_{1,10}$ | $p_{1,9}$ | $p_{1,8}$ | $p_{1,7}$ | $p_{1,6}$ | $p_{1,5}$ | $p_{1,4}$ | $p_{1,3}$ | $p_{1,2}$ | $p_{1,1}$ |

Rating of the Company on a Given Stimulus

In the table, $p_{ij}$ is the percentage of those students in the given group who have rated the given company "i" overall as a place to work who have also rated it "j" on the given stimulus. Thus,

$$\sum_{j=1}^{10} p_{ij} = 1 \text{ for every i.}$$

We interpret $p_{ij}$ as the probability that a student in the given group will rate the given company "j" on the given stimulus if he has rated it "i" overall as a place to work. It is thus a conditional probability. Hence, if a student in the group has rated the given company "8" as a place to work, then he will rate the company "10" on the given stimulus with probability $p_{8,10}$, "9" with probability $p_{8,9}$, "8" with probability $p_{8,8}$, "7" with probability $p_{8,7}$, etc.

B. *The Mechanics of the Model*

The input is now subjected to the first stage of the model, which consists of the three phases or processes already discussed.

1. The Stimulation Process

Each of the four companies concerned decides on a stimulus. Given a stimulus for each company, we subject a student to it in the following way. Four random numbers (between 0 and 1) are chosen, one for each company.

The stimulus and company in question and the group to which the student belongs determine the stimulus table to be used. The student's partisanship number $P_0^{(j)}$ determines which row of the stimulus table is applicable. Finally, the random number picks out a square in that row and a corresponding intensity or strength of stimulus $I_1^{(j)}$ (an integer from 1 to 10 obtained from the horizontal axis of the stimulus table). We illustrate by the following example. Let $P_0^{(j)}=9$, and suppose the "9" row takes on the following form:

9              | 2 | 4 | 2 | 1 | 1 | 0 | 0 | 0 | 0 | 0 |

                       10   9   8   7   6   5   4   3   2   1

Then the random number is expected to fall in the:

         "10" square 2/10's of the time

         " 9" square 4/10's of the time

         " 8" square 2/10's of the time

         " 7" sqaure 1/10 of the time

         " 6" square 1/10 of the time

         and the other squares with probability 0

Suppose that the random number falls in the "8" square, then $I_1^{(j)}=8$.

Let $I_1 = \max_{1 \leqslant j \leqslant 4} I_1^{(j)}$. In case there is no unique maximum, then we stimulate the student again with the same stimuli. If again there is no unique maximum, we use a "coin tossing" mechanism to produce a unique maximum. Once we have such a maximum, i.e., suppose $I_1 = I_1^{(j)}$ then we say that $C = j$. Thus we infer that if the student had to make a company choice as of the stimuli of the moment he would choose the jth company. We will ordinarily stimulate a student only if the chosen stimulus is one that he considers somewhat important or very important to him. However, we may stimulate all the students if we prefer.

2. The Discussion Process

Each student has assigned to him a friend chosen randomly within his group. The student has choice number, $C(S)$ and the friend, choice number $C(F)$. The rules we set up for discussion are as follows:

1. If $C(S)=C(F)$, then we say that the student and friend agree, there is no change in the student's numbers coming out of the stimulation process, and he is ready to go into the third process, the learning process.

2. If $C(S) \neq C(F)$, then we have disagreement, and the student is asked to re-evaluate his position. He does this by being restimulated with the same stimuli as before. Once restimulated, we allow him to go into the learning process without further discussion. It is possible to take the discussion process out of the model, and proceed instead directly from stimulation to learning.

3. The Learning Process

At this point each student has "interest" numbers $I_1^{(1)}$, $I_1^{(2)}$, $I_1^{(3)}$, $I_1^{(4)}$, in addition to his initial "partisanship" numbers $P_0^{(j)}$, "cumulative" numbers $\Sigma_0^{(j)}$ and "mass" numbers $K^{(j)}$. In the learning process we compute new partisanship numbers $P_1^{(j)}$ as follows:
Let $\Sigma_1^{(j)}=\Sigma_0^{(j)} + I_1^{(j)}$.
Then we define:

$$P_1^{(j)} = \frac{\Sigma_1^{(j)}}{K^{(j)}+1} - \frac{\Sigma_0^{(j)} + I_1^{(j)}}{K^{(j)}+1} = \frac{K^{(j)} P_0^{(j)} + I_1^{(j)}}{K^{(j)}+1}$$

In the case in which the student has not been stimultaed by the jth company, i.e., the case in which the stimulus chosen by the jth company is not deemed important by the student, we define $P_1^{(j)}=P_0^{(j)}$, or equivalently, set $I_1^{(j)}=P_0^{(j)}$, thus:

$$P_1^{(j)} = \frac{K^{(j)} P_0^{(j)} + P_0^{(j)}}{K^{(j)}+1} = P_0^{(j)} .$$

At this point, the student is ready to go through the second cycle or stage of stimulation, discussion and learning. Since $P_1^{(j)}$ need not be an integer, let $P_1^{(j)}$ be the integer nearest $P_1^{(j)}$. Then the appropriate row of the stimulus table to be used is determined by $P_1^{(j)}$ and so on. In the case in which the student is not stimulated, we take his interest numbers from the partisanship number of the previous stage, i.e., we let $I_n^{(j)}=P_{n-1}^{(j)}$. This is equivalent to making $P_n^{(j)}=P_{n-1}^{(j)}$ as can be verified easily. Then we proceed as above.

After n stages, the partisanship number $P_n^{(j)}$ is given by the formula:

$$P_n^{(j)} = \frac{K^{(j)} P_o^{(j)} + \sum_{i=1}^{n} I_i^{(j)}}{K^{(j)} + n} = \frac{\Sigma_n^{(j)}}{K^{(j)} + n}$$

## C. Output

For each student we will be able to read his partisanship number after each stage, e.g.:

$$P_0^{(1)}, P_0^{(2)}, \ldots ; P_1^{(1)}, P_1^{(2)}, \ldots ; \ldots \ldots ; P_n^{(1)}, P_n^{(2)} \ldots \ldots$$

Next, we will get, after each stage, each company's average partisanship number:

$$\pi_n^{(j)} = \frac{1}{234} \sum_{m=1}^{234} P_{nm}^{(j)}$$

where $P_{nm}^{(j)}$ is the partisanship number of the mth student for the jth company after the nth stage and where 234 is the sample size.

Finally, we will get the distribution for each company of the $P_n^{(j)}$'s after each stage. For this purpose, we round off the $P_n^{(j)}$'s to the nearest integer and express the number of them in each box by a percentage of the total. We also express these kinds of output by student group.

## D. Description of the Experiment

The experiment consisted of two parts. In the first part, we set out to simulate in the model the actual advertising campaigns which took place during the period in question. This turned out to be rather difficult, for various reasons. For one, it was customary to use several of the critical issues in one advertisement. All of the companies were found to be using most of the critical issues in their advertising. Another difficulty was that it was extremely hard, if not impossible, to estimate company recruitment budgets, media mixes, and the exact correspondence between frequency of advertising messages and number of cycles through which the message should be used in the model.

Because of this, we devised the idea of an "average" issue or stimulus. The stimulus tables for the average issue were computed by averaging out the corresponding entries in the stimulus tables for all of the twelve issues. For example, the average stimulus table for Company 1 and Group 1 was obtained by averaging out the corresponding entries in the Company 1-Group 1 stimulus tables for all of the twelve issues. We then used their average stimulus tables through ten cycles of the model and compared the results with the evaluations given in the second questionnaire. We give the results by group and by totals.

| Group 1 | Company I | Company II | Company III | Company IV |
|---|---|---|---|---|
| Questionnaire I | 8.54 | 7.08 | 8.67 | 7.23 |
| Questionnaire II | 8.72 | 7.49 | 8.41 | 7.31 |
| Model Prediction | 8.69 | 7.59 | 8.62 | 7.64 |

| Group 2 | Company I | Company II | Company III | Company IV |
|---|---|---|---|---|
| Questionnaire I | 8.57 | 7.14 | 7.10 | 8.04 |
| Questionnaire II | 8.94 | 7.41 | 7.51 | 7.55 |
| Model Prediction | 8.94 | 7.74 | 8.25 | 8.22 |

| Group 3 | Company I | Company II | Company III | Company IV |
|---|---|---|---|---|
| Questionnaire I | 8.43 | 7.78 | 7.86 | 7.82 |
| Questionnaire II | 8.53 | 7.73 | 7.92 | 7.41 |
| Model Prediction | 8.80 | 7.92 | 8.45 | 7.92 |

| Group 4 | Company I | Company II | Company III | Company IV |
|---|---|---|---|---|
| Questionnaire I | 7.96 | 7.57 | 7.78 | 7.74 |
| Questionnaire II | 8.83 | 7.83 | 8.30 | 7.48 |
| Model Prediction | 8.73 | 7.83 | 8.54 | 7.74 |

| Group 5 | Company I | Company II | Company III | Company IV |
|---|---|---|---|---|
| Questionnaire I | 8.43 | 7.52 | 8.39 | 7.26 |
| Questionnaire II | 8.70 | 7.65 | 8.52 | 7.39 |
| Model Prediction | 8.82 | 7.68 | 8.50 | 7.61 |

| Group 6 | Company I | Company II | Company III | Company IV |
|---|---|---|---|---|
| Questionnaire I | 8.14 | 7.23 | 7.73 | 7.18 |
| Questionnaire II | 8.59 | 7.27 | 8.18 | 7.18 |
| Model Prediction | 8.82 | 7.83 | 8.43 | 7.73 |

| Group 7 | Company I | Company II | Company III | Company IV |
|---|---|---|---|---|
| Questionnaire I | 8.76 | 7.45 | 7.14 | 6.69 |
| Questionnaire II | 9:00 | 7.52 | 7.28 | 7.21 |
| Model Prediction | 9.10 | 7.86 | 8.27 | 7.20 |

| Total | Company I | Company II | Company III | Company IV |
|---|---|---|---|---|
| Questionnaire I | 8:44 | 7.39 | 7.78 | 7.50 |
| Questionnaire II | 8.76 | 7.56 | 7.96 | 7.88 |
| Model Prediction | 8.85 | 7.78 | 8.43 | 7.78 |

As can be easily verified, the model prediction falls well within the most stringent $K^2$ goodness of fit criteria. We achieved even better results by running each of the twelve issues ten times and averaging the results, assuming that only students who thought the issue important would make a response to it. The results in this case follow.

| Group 1 | Company I | Company II | Company III | Company IV |
|---|---|---|---|---|
| Questionnaire I | 8.54 | 7.08 | 8.67 | 7.23 |
| Questionnaire II | 8.72 | 7.49 | 8.41 | 7.31 |
| Model Prediction | 8.71 | 7.43 | 8.62 | 7.57 |

| Group 2 | Company I | Company II | Company III | Company IV |
|---|---|---|---|---|
| Questionnaire I | 8.57 | 7.14 | 7.10 | 8.04 |
| Questionnaire II | 8.94 | 7.41 | 7.51 | 7.55 |
| Model Prediction | 8.79 | 7.48 | 7.97 | 8.15 |

| Group 3 | Company I | Company II | Company III | Company IV |
|---|---|---|---|---|
| Questionnaire I | 8.43 | 7.78 | 7.86 | 7.82 |
| Questionnaire II | 8.53 | 7.73 | 7.92 | 7.41 |
| Model Prediction | 8.68 | 7.83 | 8.20 | 7.98 |

| Group 4 | Company I | Company II | Company III | Company IV |
|---|---|---|---|---|
| Questionnaire I | 7.96 | 7.57 | 7.78 | 7.74 |
| Questionnaire II | 8.83 | 7.83 | 8.30 | 7.48 |
| Model Prediction | 8.42 | 7.79 | 8.23 | 7.84 |

| Group 5 | Company I | Company II | Company III | Company IV |
|---|---|---|---|---|
| Questionnaire I | 8.43 | 7.52 | 8.39 | 7.26 |
| Questionnaire II | 8.70 | 7.65 | 8.52 | 7.39 |
| Model Prediction | 8.68 | 7.67 | 8.50 | 7.65 |

| Group 6 | Company I | Company II | Company III | Company IV |
|---|---|---|---|---|
| Questionnaire I | 8.14 | 7.23 | 7.73 | 7.18 |
| Questionnaire II | 8.59 | 7.27 | 8.18 | 7.18 |
| Model Prediction | 8.69 | 7.55 | 8.24 | 7.62 |

| Group 7 | Company I | Company II | Company III | Company IV |
|---|---|---|---|---|
| Questionnaire I | 8.76 | 7.45 | 7.14 | 6.69 |
| Questionnaire II | 9:00 | 7.52 | 7.28 | 7.21 |
| Model Prediction | 8.98 | 7.62 | 7.92 | 7.31 |

| Total | Company I | Company II | Company III | Company IV |
|---|---|---|---|---|
| Questionnaire I | 8:44 | 7.39 | 7.78 | 7.50 |
| Questionnaire II | 8.76 | 7.56 | 7.96 | 7.38 |
| Model Prediction | 8.72 | 7.62 | 8.23 | 7.79 |

In the second part of the experiment, we took each issue and ran it through the model ten times for each company. Thus, we started with Issue 1, "the company's standing in your field of career interest," and we let each of the companies use this issue through ten cycles of the model. Then we started anew with Issue 2 and did the same thing. And so on, through Issue 12.

We did this part of the experiment in two ways. In the first way, we let each of the students be stimulated by the given issues. In the second way, we stimulated a student with an issue if he felt the issue was important to him. We will summarize some of the results.

First of all, we defined an issue to be a good one for a given company if through the use of it the company's average overall rating went up more than 5 per cent. We defined the issue as being a better one for a company than for another company if its percentage rise was greater than that of the company.

Thus, in comparing Company 3 with Company 1, its main competitor, we found the following breakdown useful.

|  | Company 3 Better Than Company 1 | Company 3 Not as Good as Company 1 |  |
|---|---|---|---|
| Good Issues | Quality of products<br>Standing in field of career interest<br><br>Drive to achieve goals | Challenging work<br>Caliber of personnel<br><br>Basic research | Company Issues |
| Poor Issues | Starting Salary<br><br>Training Program<br>Consideration of Employees<br>Rapid Advancement | Encouragement of Ingenuity<br>Aid to Education | Individual Issues |
|  | Business Image | Scientific Image |  |

Thus, Company 3's good issues are "quality of products, standing in field of career interest, drive to achieve goals, challenging work, caliber of personnel, basic research," which are basically issues relating to how good a company it is. Its poor issues are "starting salary, training program, consideration of employees, rapid advancement, encouragement of ingenuity, aid to education" which are issues relating to how good a company it is for the individual.

Also, the issues in which Company 3 is better than Company 1 are "quality of products, standing in field of career interest, drive to achieve goals, starting salary, training programs, consideration of employees, and rapid advancement." which are issues having to do with its business image. But the issues in which Company 3 does not do as well as Company 1 are "challenging work, caliber of personnel, basic research, encouragement of ingenuity, aid to education" whcih are issues having to do with its scientific image.

In its advertising against Company 1, Company 3 can best afford to stress the issues in the upper left-hand box: "quality of product, standing in field of career interest, drive to achieve goals." The issues in the upper right-hand box, "challenging work, caliber of personnel, basic research" are also good issues for Company 3. However, they represent a "trap" for it, since Company 1 is stronger than they are in those issues. In fact, the basic research issues have so been pre-empted by Company 1 that Company 3's use of them calls attention to Company 1's excellence in them.

The issues in the lower left-hand box; "starting salary, training program, consideration of employees, rapid advancement," are not particularly good for Company 3 but Company 1 is no better, so that stressing these issues causes small gains for Company 3 as opposed to Company 1. Finally, the issues in the lower right-hand box, "encouragement of ingenuity and aid to education," are bad ones for Company 3 in which Company 1 is better. These issues represent a product problem for Company 3 in relation to Company 1. They are issues in which Company 3 will have to make basic changes before using them.

If we compare Company 3 with all of its 3 competitors, we get the following (see table, p. 133):

The numbers in parentheses represent the companies that are better than Company 3.

Here it is seen that there are three issues which are good ones for Company 3 in which it does better than all of its competitors, namely: "quality of products, standing in field of career interest, drive to achieve goals." Those are obviously Company 3's best opportunities for improving its standing against all its competitors.

|  | Company 3 Better Than Competitors | Company 3 Not as Good as Competitors |
|---|---|---|
| Good Issues | Quality of Products<br><br>Standing in field of Career Interest<br><br>Drive to Achieve Goals | Challenging work (1)<br><br>Caliber of Personnel (1)<br><br>Basic Research (1) |
| Poor Issues | Starting Salary | Encouragement of Ingenuity (1, 4)<br><br>Aid to Education (1, 2, 4)<br><br>Training Program (2)<br><br>Consideration of Employees (2, 4)<br><br>Rapid Advancement (2) |

The issues in the upper right-hand box, "challenging work, caliber of personnel, basic research," are good ones for Company 3, but it loses ground to Company 1, when both are using them. However, it does gain on Companies 2 and 4. Company 1 seems to have pre-empted those issues.

In the lower left-hand box, there is the issue, "starting salary," which is not a particularly good one for Company 3; however, it does gain on all of its competitors through the use of it. This represents an area for possible education of the population.

Finally, in the lower right-hand box are issues which are not so good for Company 3, and in which some competitor does better. In fact, the issue, "encouragement of ingenuity," is one in which both Company 1 and Company 4 do better. All three competitors do better on "aid to education." Companies 2 and 4 do better on "consideration of employees," Company 2 does better on "training program" and "rapid advancement."

Let us see how the issues divide up for the other three companies.

## Company 1

|  | Company 1 Better Than Competitors | Some Competitor Better Than Company 1 |
|---|---|---|
| Good Issues | Challenging Work<br><br>Basic Research<br><br>Encouragmeent of Ingenuity<br><br>Caliber of Personnel | Quality of Products (3, 4) |
| Poor Issues |  | Aids to Education (2, 4)<br><br>Drive to Achieve Goals (2, 3, 4)<br>Training Programs (2, 3, 4)<br><br>Standing in Field of Career Interest (2, 3, 4)<br><br>Starting Salary (2, 3, 4)<br><br>Consideration of Employees (2, 3, 4)<br><br>Rapid Advancement (2, 3, 4) |

This shows that Company 1's good issues are "challenging work, basic research, encouragement of ingenuity, calibre of personnel, and quality of products." Of those, the first four are issues in which it does better than all of its competitors. In the last issues, "quality of products," there are two companies, Companies 3 and 4, which do better. Its good issues tend to be relating to how good a scientific company it is.

Company 1's poor issues are "aid to education, drive to achieve goals, training program, standing in field of career interest, starting salary, consideration of employees, and rapid advancement." Oddly enough, Company 1 does not top any of its competitors in any of these issues. In fact, it is topped by all of its competitors in all of the issues except for "aid to education" where Company 2 and 4 do better. Company 1's poor issues tend to be issues having to do with its business characteristics and its dealings with the individual.

## Company 2

|  | Company 2 Better Than Competitors | Some Competitor Better Than Company 2 |
|---|---|---|
| Good Issues | Aid to Education<br><br>Training Programs | Quality of Products (1, 3, 4) |
| Poor Issues | Rapid Advancement | Drive to Achieve Goals (3, 4)<br><br>Caliber of Personnel (1, 3)<br><br>Encouragement of Ingenuity (1, 3, 4)<br><br>Basic Research (1, 3)<br><br>Challenging Work (1, 3, 4)<br><br>Standing in Field of Career Interest (3, 4)<br><br>Starting Salary (3, 4)<br><br>Consideration of Employees (3, 4) |

Company 2's good issues are "aid to education, training program, and quality of products." Of these, it is better than all of its competitors in the first two. In the third one, "quality of products," it is excelled by all three of its competitors.

Company 2's poor issues are "rapid advancement, drive to achieve goals, caliber of personnel, encouragement of ingenuity, basic research, challenging work, standing in field of career interest, starting salary, and consideration of employees." However, the first of these, "rapid advancement," is one in which it does better than its competitors. This gives it a possible issue to use in an educational way. In the remaining issues, there are at least two competitors that do better in each.

Company 2's best issues seem to deal with the help it gives the individual to improve himself.

Finally, let us look at Company 4.

## Company 4

|  | Company 4 Better Than Competitors | Some Competitor Better Than Company 4 |
|---|---|---|
| Good Issues |  | Quality of Products (3) Encouragement of Ingenuity (1) Drive to Achieve Goals (3) Standing in Field of Career Interest (3) Aid to Education (2) |
| Poor Issues | Consideration of Employees | Challenging Work (1, 3) Caliber of Personnel (1, 2, 3) Basic Research (1, 2, 3) Starting Salary (3) Training Programs (2, 3) Rapid Advancement (2, 3) |

Company 4's good issues are "quality of products, encouragement of ingenuity, drive to achieve goals, standing in field of career interest and aid to education." However, in each of these there is a competitor which does better.

Its poor issues are "consideration of employees, challenging work, caliber of personnel, basic research, starting salary, training programs, and rapid advancement." Of these, Company 4 does better than all of its competitors in the issue, "consideration of employees," and worse than some competitor in the others.

The reader—will note that the issue, "quality of products" is a good one for all four companies, while the issues, "rapid advancement and starting salary" are poor ones for all of the companies.

# A Decision-Theoretic Analysis of a Problem in Political Campaigning

GERALD H. KRAMER

*University of Rochester*

1.1   In the past two decades, the use of quantitative methods as aids for decision-making has become common in many fields, particularly those involving industrial and military operations. More recently, efforts have been made to apply these methods to other governmental activities.[1] By and large, however, these efforts have not been made by political scientists, nor have the methods employed, despite their increasing sophistication and power, had great impact upon the discipline. This is unfortunate, for many of the traditional concerns of political scientists appear to be quite susceptible to this sort of analysis. In this paper, we will attempt to show how such a quantitative decision-theoretic approach might be used to analyze a practical political problem, namely the problem of conducting a door-to-door canvass of voters, for partisan campaign purposes.

Such a demonstration may be of interest for two reasons. First, it may lead to results which are of substantive or practical interest to the student of political campaigning. In the course of our analysis we will suggest some rough rules of thumb and then develop a systematic optimization procedure for efficient canvassing; we will also offer some tentative conclusions concerning the relative efficiencies of several simpler canvassing strategies, and indicate the relevance of our findings to other campaign problems.

The demonstration may also be of broader methodological interest. In political science there has been considerable debate and discussion as to whether certain concepts can be quantified, or certain problems studied quantitatively. In fact, there is no reason to doubt that quantitative research—of some kind—*can* be done on almost any problem; the only interesting questions are whether it

---

[1] For examples, see R. N. McKean, *Efficiency in Government Through Systems Analysis* (New York: Wiley, 1958); H. G. Schaller, ed., *Public Expenditure Decisions in the Urban Community* (Baltimore: Johns Hopkins Press, 1963); and chaps. vii and xiii of D. B. Hertz and R. T. Eddison, eds., *Progress in Operations Research*, Vol. II (New York: Wiley, 1964).

*should* be done, and *how*. But these questions—as R. L. Ackoff, for example, convincingly argues[2]—cannot be satisfactorily understood except by examining them in the context of the *uses* to which the research results are ultimately to be put. We will not be specifically concerned with methodological questions here. Nevertheless, by focusing explicitly on the question of uses, and by showing one way in which quantitative empirical results can be applied to solve a specific problem, we may at least be able to indicate a perspective, by means of which some of the methodological issues of quantitative empirical research may come to be better understood.

1.2   The organization of this study is as follows: in section 2 we formulate the overall problem of resource allocation in political campaigning, within a general decision-theoretic framework. We then narrow the focus to canvassing, and in section 3 develop a simple quantitative model of a political canvass. In section 4 we describe a general technique, based upon the model, which systematically discovers the optimal allocation of canvassing effort, in any constituency and for any budget size. We also describe some simpler canvassing strategies, and then demonstrate and compare all of these approaches by applying each to a hypothetical constituency. This analysis is based upon a number of simplifying assumptions; in section 5 we explore the question of how our conclusions are affected when these simplifying assumptions are relaxed, in various ways. Finally, some brief concluding remarks are offered in section 6.

2.1   In general terms, we can describe a decision problem as follows: we have a decision-maker, who is confronted with a set of alternative, mutually exclusive courses of action, and who is interested in attaining certain possibly conflicting goals or objectives. The available alternatives are related to the objectives, perhaps in complex and uncertain ways; the decision-maker's problem is to select that alternative which is "best" in terms of his goals. Quantitative analysis of such a problem requires that we provide a concise description of the problem, a precise criterion of "best," and finally, a systematic way to use this information to discover which alternative is in fact best. A comprehensive solution to the overall

---

[2] R. L. Ackoff, S.K. Gupta, and J. S. Minas, *Scientific Method: Optimizing Applied Research Decisions* (New York: Wiley, 1962).

problem of conducting a political campaign is hardly feasible at present. However, as a first step toward that ultimate goal, and also as background for the more detailed treatment of canvassing in sections 3 to 5, let us briefly attempt a preliminary formulation of the overall problem.

2.2   The range of alternatives confronting a candidate running for office is truly enormous. Among the subjects dealt with in one well-known campaign manual, for example, are the following: registration drives, mail campaigns, house-to-house canvassing, bumper sticker campaigns, special group activities, coffee parties, larger receptions, plant visits, sound trucks, meetings and debates, television, telephone campaigns, voter transportation, and poll watching.[3] Each such activity can be carried out in a variety of ways, and the purpose of a campaign manual is presumably to describe some of the more efficient ways.

In addition to these various tactical questions, there is also the broader strategic question of deciding between activities. If our resources are limited, then to increase the scale of one activity (e.g., to make more use of TV) means we must cut back on some other activity (e.g., plan a smaller canvass); somehow, we must decide which activities to increase and which to cut back, in order to achieve a balanced overall campaign strategy. Let us suppose that there are n distinct activities, and that for each we have a quantitative measure of the overall *level* of the activity—e.g., so many man-hours of canvassing, or hours of TV, etc. Then we can concisely represent any campaign strategy by its activity levels $X_1, ..., X_n$. The set of all possible strategies is the set of all such n-tuples, and the set of *available* strategies is the subset of such n-tuples which are feasible in terms of the resources available. Thus, if the only resource which is limited is money, and if the $i^{th}$ activity costs $C_i$ dollars per unit, $i=1, 2,..., n$, then the set of available strategies is set of n-tuples which satisfy

$$\sum_{i=1}^{n} C_i X_i \leq B,$$

where B is the maximum possible campaign budget, in dollars. The campaign problem is to determine which of these n-tuples is "best," according to some well-defined criterion of "best."

[3] *The Democratic Campaign Manual 1964* (Washington, D. C.: Democratic National Committee, c. 1964).

2.3 Just as there are many ways of running a campaign, so also there is a variety of possible goals which a candidate may be pursuing. No doubt most candidates are interested in winning the election. Even so, a third-party candidate, for example, may have no real hope of winning, and may therefore gear his campaign strategy to other goals, such as getting his "message" across, or depriving one of the major-party candidates of votes. Even a serious contender for office may place great stress upon factors other than success, such as "educating" his constituents, whatever the electoral consequences. But however important such goals may be in specific instances, if a general analysis is to proceed we must concentrate upon the major and most tangible of the goals. For most candidates in most contests this goal is clearly to win.

Political campaigning is an uncertain business, in which no campaign strategy can guarantee victory. Thus one plausible quantitative translation of the goal of winning, which takes this uncertainty into account, is that the candidate wishes, in selecting his campaign strategy, to maximize his *probability* of winning. An alternative, though related, formulation is that the candidate wishes to maximize the size of his *plurality* (or more precisely, since uncertainty is present, his *expected* plurality $E(n_A - n_B)$ where $n_A$ and $n_B$ are the votes cast for A and B, respectively, and where E is the expected-value operator.[4])

With the usual electoral arrangements, winning is normally closely related to the size of the candidate's plurality. However, these two formulations of the candidate's goal, though related, may nevertheless lead to differing recommendations when used to assess the value of alternative campaign tactics. This is particularly likely if one of the tactics is very risky, but also potentially very productive. For example, suppose the choice facing the candidate is between adopting such a tactic $(t_1)$, versus continuing present tactics $(t_2)$; moreover, suppose the candidate now has 55% of the votes and will maintain this lead for sure with $t_2$. Tactic $t_1$, on the other hand, will either gain another 40% or lose 10% of the vote, each with probability .5. If his goal is to maximize his expected plurality, the proper choice is to adopt $t_1$, since his expected plurality is 40%

---

[4] The expected value of a function is its average, defined by
$$E(f) = \sum_x x \Pr(f=x).$$
See, e.g., J. G. Kemeny, *et. al.*, *Finite Mathematical Structures* (Englewood Cliffs, N. J.: Prentice-Hall, 1961).

then versus 10% with $t_2$. On the other hand, choosing $t_1$ over $t_2$ reduces the probability of winning from 1.0 to .5, and therefore if the goal is to maximize his probability of winning, exactly the opposite recommendation is in order. Other things being equal, presumably most candidates would take the more conservative course and adopt $t_2$; in that sense, the probabilistic objective is the more realistic.

However, this formulation is computationally quite difficult to work with; in practical applications one would have to resort to simulation techniques which are expensive and often cumbersome. The expected-plurality criterion is much simpler in this respect, and possesses the convenient property that if we can evaluate the candidate's expected plurality in each of several subunits (e.g., precincts) in his constituency, then his overall plurality can be obtained by simple summation. Clearly this is not true of the probabilistic criterion. Moreover, the expected-plurality criterion is more easily comprehended and communicated, since campaigners traditionally think in terms of so many votes gained or lost, and the criterion translates directly into these terms. Either formulation provides us with a reasonable, quantitative value criterion; however, in subsequent discussion we shall employ the expected-plurality criterion.

2.4   Suppose the following: that we have settled on a value criterion V; that, after extensive empirical analysis, we are able to predict what level of V will result from implementing any particular campaign strategy $X_1, X_2, ..., X_n$; that activity i, $i = 1, 2, ..., n$, costs $C_i$ dollars per unit (man-hour, TV-minute, or whatnot); and that the total cost of whatever strategy we adopt shall not exceed our budget B. The candidate wishes to find the best feasible strategy; thus the overall campaign problem is to find $X_1, ..., X_n$ such that

$$V (X_1, ..., X_n) = \text{maximum},$$
subject to                                                                      (2.1)
$$\Sigma C_i X_i \leqslant B.$$

Under certain reasonably general assumptions about the function $V (X_1, X_2, ..., X_n)$,[5] the following will be true: at the maximum, the

---

[5] Specifically we assume V to be continuous, increasing, and concave, and every activity to be sufficiently productive so that the problem of corner maxima does not arise. See, e.g., the Appendix, "The Simple Mathematics of Maximization," in C. J. Hitch and R. N. McKean, *The Economics of Defense in the Nuclear Age* (Cambridge: Harvard University Press, 1961).

marginal increase in V produced by spending an additional dollar on any activity must equal that produced in any other activity. Conversely, if the marginal increase in some activity i is less than that in another activity j, then clearly we can obtain a better strategy by reallocating funds from i to j (unless the allocation to i is already zero dollars, in which case further reallocation is impossible). These marginal increases, or marginal productivities, play an important role in discovering and verifying a solution to (2.1). Hence in studying campaigning, or any of the various campaign activities, one important aim of the analysis is to provide a basis for calculating these marginal productivities.

3.1   To demonstrate how such an analysis might proceed, we will examine one of these activities in greater detail. The problem which we consider is that of conducting a precinct-level door-to-door canvass of voters during a campaign, in order to pass out literature, reinforce the faithful and convert the opposition, and so on. In conducting a drive of this sort there are a number of choices to be faced, concerning which areas of the constituency shall be canvassed, what type of literature and of approach shall be employed, which routes shall be assigned to which workers, and so forth. Here, we consider only the two broadest problems, concerning the choice of localities and of "tactics," a term to be defined below.

   Conducting a canvass requires the expenditure of various kinds of resources, such as labor, printed materials, etc. We assume that it is always possible to obtain additional quantities of any of these resources, at fixed costs, if necessary; hence the only resource limitation we need consider is the overall budget constraint. A canvassing budget of given size can be employed in a variety of ways, producing a variety of different effects. Our problem here is to determine—or more accurately, to obtain a method for determining—which of these possible ways is "best," in terms of the expected plurality produced. As a first step in this endeavor, we proceed now to construct a model of a political canvass, with which we can assess the effects of alternative canvassing strategies.

3.2   By a model of a canvass, we mean a symbolic representation of the process, which can be manipulated for predictive purposes. The elements of our model are the following: we assume the electorate to be partioned into a number k of small, relatively homogeneous units such as precincts or voting districts. In the $i^{th}$ precinct, let

$N^i$ be the number of residents,
$P_R^i$ be the fraction of registered voters, of whom
$P_V^i$ actually vote, and
$P_A^i$ and $P_B^i$ prefer parties A and B respectively.

Where we are speaking of a single precinct and no ambiguity will result, we will usually omit the superscripts. Notice that, as of the time of the canvass, the quantities $P_A, P_B, P_V$ are predicted rather than actual values; they are forecasts of what will happen several days or weeks hence, on election day. These predictions need not be extremely accurate; extrapolation from past comparable elections would suffice. We assume that it is possible to make these predictions about each precinct, at negligible cost. We also assume that it is possible, though not necessarily inexpensive, to determine for individual voters within the district whether they are registered, and which party they prefer. In a well-organized precinct, this is the type of information which would be contained in the party's card file; in an unorganized precinct, it might be possible to use official registration data (where partisan registration is in effect), or it might be necessary to conduct a precampaign canvass. Again, this information on individual voters need not be perfectly accurate, though for simplicity we will assume, initially, that it is. We also assume that in any single homogeneous precinct, turnout and partisanship are statistically independent.

Next, we assume that within any single precinct there are two basic tactics available to the party conducting the canvass. In the first, which we will refer to as a "blind" canvass, the party systematically contacts every person in the precinct, irrespective of registration and partisanship. The second tactic is a "selective" canvass, in which only registered partisans of the party are contacted. Clearly there are other possibilities as well, such as contacting all registered voters or attempting to contact only the habitual nonvoters within the precinct. Here, however, we will consider only the two representative tactics described above.

Our model must finally take into account the response of the individual voters in the constituency to contact by a party worker. Many different kinds of effect are possible, e.g., upon the voters' motivations and attitudes, his knowledge, or his subsequent behavior. For our purposes, however, only those responses which affect our candidate's plurality in the forthcoming election are immediately relevant; hence, we ignore the various possible psychological effects and confine ourselves to the question of how partisan contact affects the recipient's subsequent voting behavior. It is useful to distinguish between two possible types of voting-behavior effect, which we shall refer to as *preference* and *turnout* effects. By a preference effect, we mean any alteration in a voter's candidate preference—or, more precisely, in the probability that, if he votes, he will cast his ballot for a given candidate. By a turnout effect, we mean any alteration in the probability that he will vote at all, for either candidate.

Obviously, the questions of the existence and of the magnitudes of these effects are empirical questions, and can only be settled by empirical investigation. In fact, several such investigations have been performed by various researchers. It would be too much of a diversion, here, to review the methods and results of each of these studies; in summary, however, they seem to show the following: Preference effects, in contested partisan elections, are small and statistically insignificant in magnitude, and do not follow any consistent pattern in direction. Henceforth we will ignore them. Sizable turnout effects, however, do apparently exist. These effects are positive, in the sense of increasing (rather than decreasing) turnout probabilities, and for practical purposes their magnitudes can be taken to be independent of such factors as the partisanship of the contact or of the recipient, or the level of the office being contested.[6] For our purposes, of course, we need a precise and quantitative description of these effects. The following simple model is convenient to work with and has proven to be a realistic formulation empirically:

$$\Pr(V|C) = \Pr(V|\overline{C}) + \alpha[1 - \Pr(V|\overline{C})] \tag{3.1}$$

Here, $\Pr(V|\overline{C})$ is the probability of voting in the absence of contact, $\Pr(V|C)$ is the probability of voting after having been contacted, and $\alpha$ is a parameter. In terms of relative frequencies, the model asserts that if a large group of voters is canvassed, then the final turnout rate will equal the precontact rate $\Pr(V|\overline{C})$, plus a certain fraction $\alpha$ of that portion of the group which would not otherwise have voted. That is, the rate (or probability) of non-

---

[6]For a summary of most of the available evidence, see G. H. Kramer, "Decision-Theoretic Analysis of Canvassing and Other Precinct-Level Activities in Political Campaigning" (Doctoral dissertation; MIT, 1965), chaps. iii and iv.

voting is reduced by a constant fraction $\alpha$. Evidently the pre-contact turnout probabilities (and therefore also the postcontact probabilities) can vary from voter to voter, or precinct to precinct; however, $\alpha$ is constant for all voters and for all precincts. Empirically, a typical or average value of $\alpha$ is .4.[7] (Clearly we are speaking here only of registered voters, since both the pre- and postcontact turnout probabilities of unregistered voters are always zero.)

3.3 The value criterion which we wish to maximize is the candidate's constituency-wide expected plurality. This overall plurality equals the sum of the candidate's sub-pluralities in each precinct; hence let us initially consider the effects of our tactics in a single precinct. If we use $P_V$ as the value of $Pr(V|\overline{C})$ and $P_A$ as the probability of voting for candidate A, for a voter drawn at random from the precinct in question, then evidently the expected plurality for A in the absence of a canvass is

$$P_A P_V P_R N - P_B P_V P_R N = (P_A - P_B) P_V P_R N$$

If we assume a pure two-party system, where $P_A + P_B = 1$, then this reduces to

$$(P_A - [1 - P_A]) P_V P_R N = (2P_A - 1) P_V P_R N \qquad (3.2)$$

Now suppose that the entire precinct is canvassed blindly—that is, all voters are contacted, regardless of affiliation. Evidently the effect of such a canvass is to increase the turnout probability somewhat, according to

$$Pr(V|C) = Pr(V|\overline{C}) + \alpha[1 - Pr(V|\overline{C})]$$
$$= P_V + \alpha(1 - P_V)$$

Hence the expected plurality becomes

$$[2P_A - 1][P_V + \alpha(1 - P_V)]P_R N,$$

and the net *addition* to the candidate's plurality resulting from the canvass is

$$[2P_A - 1][P_V + \alpha(1 - P_V)]P_R N - [2P_A - 1]P_V P_R N$$
$$= \alpha[1 - P_V][2P_A - 1]P_R N \qquad (3.3)$$

More generally we can divide this expression by the number of voters contacted, N, to obtain the *net votes gained per contact* (or productivity per contact, $\rho_1$) for a blind canvass:

$$\rho_1 = \alpha(1 - P_V)(2P_A - 1)P_R. \qquad (3.4)$$

Now suppose that a selective canvass is used, in which only

[7] *Ibid.*, especially pp. 72-75.

registered A-partisans are contacted. After the canvass, the expected plurality is evidently

$$(P_V + \alpha[1 - P_V])P_A P_R N - P_V(1 - P_A)P_R N$$
$$= \alpha[1 - P_V]P_A P_R N + (2P_A - 1)P_V P_R N.$$

By subtracting (3.2) we obtain the addition to the candidate's plurality produced by the canvass, and by dividing this by the number, $P_A P_R N$, of voters contacted we have the per-contact productivity for a selective canvass,

$$\rho_2 = \alpha(1 - P_V) \tag{3.5}$$

Note that $\rho_1$, unlike $\rho_2$, can become negative because of the $(2P_A - 1)$ term; in neighborhoods where the party has only minority support, blind canvassing is counterproductive. Both expressions contain a $(1 - P_V)$ term, and hence either type of canvass is relatively more effective in low-turnout neighborhoods, and also in off-year elections.

Finally, let $c_1$ and $c_2$ be the costs per contact of conducting blind and selective canvasses, respectively, where presumably $c_2 > c_1$. As expenditure on either tactic increases, evidently the gain in plurality increases initially with slope $\rho_1/c_1$ or $\rho_2/c_2$. Eventually, when all suitable voters in the precinct have been contacted, further increases in expenditure produce no additional gains in plurality. Graphically, the overall gain-cost relations are as shown in Figure 3.1 (for a precinct for which $P_A > .5$).

FIGURE 3.1

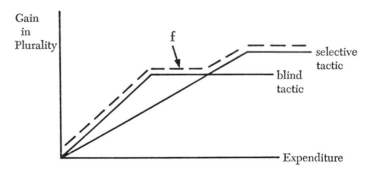

4.1 Our model enables us to determine the consequences of any particular allocation of resources to precincts and tactics, and because of the very simple structure of the model, these consequences can be readily traced out by hand calculation. Our purpose in constructing the model was to use it in order to find the best, or optimal, allocation; thus, in principle, we might try to enumerate systematically every possible allocation, use the model to predict the expected gain in plurality produced by each, and finally select that allocation with the greatest gain. Obviously such an approach is tedious at best, and furthermore there is no assurance that it will ever discover the best allocation, since there are infinitely many possibilities to be tried. It would clearly be desirable to have an efficient and systematic method for discovering the optimal allocation without the necessity of an exhaustive search of the alternatives. We proceed now to describe such a method.

4.2 In our overall optimization problem, we must decide how to allocate our resources across precincts, and also which tactic shall be employed in each precinct. Let us first consider the latter question; from inspection of Figure 3.1 it is evident that, in a precinct of the type depicted, if the expenditure in the precinct is large then the selective tactic will be preferred. The maximum gain possible from blind canvassing (when every voter in the precinct is contacted) is given by the maximum possible number of such contacts, N, times the per-contact productivity, $\rho_1$; thus, using (3.4), the maximum gain is

$$\rho_1 N = \alpha (2 P_A - 1)(1 - P_V) P_R N. \tag{4.1}$$

In selective canvassing the maximum number of contacts is the number of registered A-partisans, $P_A P_R N$, and the per-contact productivity is $\rho_2$, so from (3.5), the maximum gain is

$$\rho_2 P_A P_R N = \alpha (1 - P_V) P_A P_R N. \tag{4.2}$$

Whenever $P_A < 1$, evidently this latter expression is larger. When expenditure levels are large enough so that the precinct can be "saturated," the blind canvass is inferior because it inevitably activates some opposition voters, whereas a selective canvass does not. Conversely, in Figure 3.1 the blind canvass is better at low expenditure levels because of its lower cost per contact. Whether this is also true in other precincts depends critically upon the relative costs per contact, upon the registration rate (since contacts with unregistered persons, however cheap, are wasted), and upon the relative number of opposition voters in the precinct. If $P_A < .5$ then a blind canvass will be counter-productive and the selective canvass will be the preferred tactic at all expenditure levels. In general, comparing the respective per-dollar productivities $\rho_1/c_1$ and $\rho_2/c_2$, a blind canvass will be preferred (at low levels of expenditure) if and only if

$$(2P_A - 1)P_R > \frac{c_1}{c_2}$$

for the precinct in question. Let $f_i(X_i)$ be the function which predicts the plurality gain in precinct i produced by spending $X_i$ dollars on a canvass with the preferred tactic; graphically, $f_i$ will be the envelope of the gain-cost functions shown in Figure (3.1), represented by the dotted line labeled "f."

Now consider the broader question, of how our canvassing effort shall be allocated across precincts. Formally, the problem is to allocate the available canvassing budget B to the k precincts in such a way as to make the total plurality gain F as large as possible; thus,

$$F = \sum_{i=1}^{k} f_i(X_i) = \text{maximum},$$

subject to                                                                    (4.3)

1. $\sum_{i=1}^{k} X_i \leqslant B$
2. $X_i \geqslant 0, i = 1, \ldots, k$

This is a familiar constrained-maximization type of problem; however, the function to be maximized is not sufficiently smooth to permit use of the calculus to find the maximum. Other techniques, such as linear programming, do deal with piece-wise linear functions, such as we have here; unfortunately, however, in the present problem some of the payoff functions $f_i$ are not concave.[8] Without going into details, this means that (4.3), despite its very elementary structure, in fact constitutes a problem in nonlinear programming, and a solution procedure would be complicated. To circumvent these difficulties we will modify the problem somewhat, making it soluble by a much simpler procedure. The modification consists of replacing the true payoff functions $f_i$ by new, approximate functions $f_i'$, which are concave. In precincts where the selective tactic is always better, the true function $f_i$ is already concave, so in this case $f_i'$ and $f_i$ are identical. Where the blind tactic is

---

[8] A concave function is one which, roughly speaking, obeys a law of diminishing returns; specifically a function f is concave if and only if the chord which connects any two points of the function lies on or below the function between those points. On the relevance of concavity to programming, see any standard text, or, e.g., H. M. Markowitz and A. S. Manne, "On The Solution of Discrete Programming Problems," *Econometrica*, XXV (1957), 84 ff.

better initially, however, $f_i$ is not concave, so we replace it by a concave function $f_i'$; hence in this case the concave approximation $f'$ will be related to the true function $f$ as shown in Figure 4.1.

FIGURE 4.1

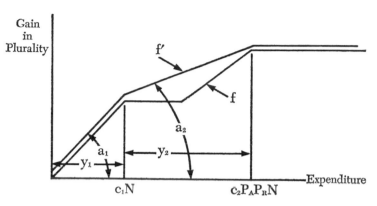

We can write $f'$ as a weighted sum

$$f_i'(X_i) = a_{i1} y_{i1} + a_{i2} y_{i2},$$

where $a_{i1}$, $a_{i2}$ are the slopes of the two line segments, and where

$$X_i = y_{i1} + y_{i2},$$
$$0 \leqslant y_{i1} \leqslant c_i N^i,$$
$$0 \leqslant y_{i2} \leqslant c_2 P_A^i P_R^i N^i - c_i N^i.$$

In precincts where the selective tactic is always best, evidently

$$f_i'(X_i) = a_{i1} y_{i1}$$

Our modified problem is thus

$$F' = \Sigma\Sigma ay = \text{maximum}$$

subject to

$$1. \ \Sigma\Sigma y \leqslant B \qquad\qquad\qquad\qquad (4.4)$$
$$2. \ 0 \leqslant y \leqslant c_i N \text{ or } c_2 P_A P_R N - c_i N$$

where $a$, $y$ are as defined above. This modified problem is readily solved by the following simple algorithm: First, evaluate $a_{i1}$, $a_{i2}$, $c_i N$, $c_2 P_A P_R N$ for each precinct; second, arrange the $a$'s in order of decreasing size

$$a_{(ij)1} \geqslant a_{(ij)2} \geqslant a_{(ij)3} \geqslant \ldots;$$

and finally, for any budget B, invest in the $y$'s in the same order, setting each at its maximum and then going on to the next on the list, until the budget is exhausted. When this procedure is complete, we will have some $y_{ij}$'s which have been set to their maximum values, some which are zero, and perhaps one (the last one on the list before the budget ran out) which is less than maximal but greater than zero. In any precinct, if $y_{i2} > 0$, then we should spend $y_{i1} + y_{i2}$ dollars on a selective canvass in that precinct; if $y_{i2} = 0$ and $y_{i1} > 0$, then we should spend $y_{i1}$ dollars on a blind canvass; and if $y_{i1} + y_{i2} = 0$, no canvassing should be done in that precinct (since the money is better spent elsewhere).

It is straightforward to show that the allocation resulting from this procedure is indeed a solution to (4.4); if $y^*$ is the first y in the sequence which has not been made as large as possible, and $a^*$ is its slope, their reallocating X dollars into some of the unused y's will increase the gain by $\leqslant a^*X$ (since the a for all unused y are $\leqslant a^*$), while the loss produced by withdrawing these dollars from earlier y will be $\geqslant a^*X$ (since the earlier a's are all $\geqslant a^*$); hence no such allocation can increase the objective function, and the original allocation is indeed a maximum.

However, (4.4) involves the concave approximations f′ rather than the true payoff functions f, and it is possible that a solution to (4.4) is still not optimal in terms of the original formulation (4.3). Our concave approximations are such that

$$f(X) \leqslant f'(X), \tag{4.5}$$

for any X. When $X=0$, or $c_1 N$, or $c_2 P_A P_R N$ (or more precisely, where the corresponding y's are either zero or as large as possible) then f and f′ are equal. Let us choose our budget B so that this is the case in every precinct, and let $z_1, ..., z_k$ be the resulting allocation; then since $f(z)=f'(z)$ in each precinct, it follows by summing over precincts that

$$\Sigma f'(z) = \Sigma f(z) \tag{4.6}$$

Now suppose we reallocate in some fashion, so that the allocation in precinct i becomes $z_i + d_i$ dollars, and where

$$\Sigma d_i \leqslant 0 \tag{4.7}$$

(since we are not to exceed the budget constraint). By the argument of the last paragraph, no such reallocation can increase the concave-approximation payoff; hence

$$\Sigma f'(z+d) \leqslant \Sigma f'(z) \tag{4.8}$$

However, letting $X = z + d$ in (4.5) and summing, evidently

$$\Sigma f(z+d) \leqslant \Sigma f'(z+d) \tag{4.9}$$

Hence if we combine this with (4.6) and (4.7), we have

$$\Sigma f(z+d) \leqslant \Sigma f'(z+d) \leqslant \Sigma f'(z) = \Sigma f(z),$$

so that for this choice of B, no reallocation can increase the true payoff $\Sigma f(z)$. For other budget levels it follows from (4.8) and (4.9) that the true gain will be less than, or possibly equal to, the solution to the modified problem (4.4).

What we have shown, then, is the following: by reformulating the original problem we obtained a modified problem which is readily solved by a simple clerical procedure. For certain budget sizes, the allocation obtained by solving the modified problem is optimal with respect to the original problem (4.3) also; for other budgets we tend to overestimate the true gain produced by the recommended allocation. Even so, however, the allocation is near-optimal, in the sense that in only one precinct (or more precisely, one of the $y_{ij}$) will resources have been committed in a less-than-optimal manner. For practical purposes, then, we have a solution procedure for our canvassing model. In section 4.4 we will apply the procedure to a hypothetical constituency.

4.3   The algorithm described above produces canvasses in which both inter-precinct resource allocation and intra-precinct tactical choice have been optimized. Though the procedure is simple to apply, nevertheless it does require more clerical and computational effort than would be needed if a simpler canvassing strategy were used. A relevant question, therefore, is whether this type of formal optimization is worth the extra effort it requires. To gain some insight into this question, let us consider some alternative, simpler canvassing strategies. The approach described in the preceeding section, in which both inter-precinct resource allocation and tactical choice are optimized, we shall refer to as "full" optimization.

At the opposite extreme, the simplest type of canvass is one in which all canvassing is blind, and is conducted upon arbitrarily or randomly selected voters. There is reason to believe that a great deal of canvassing in American elections is done blindly, and while clearly we would not expect any sensible party to select precincts at random in the literal sense, by means of a random number table, nevertheless it may be that whether a voter is canvassed or not depends upon factors which are essentially unrelated to productivity or efficiency, such as the availability of volunteers or a block captain locally, or the state of the organization in the precinct. If this is so, then taking the voters to be chosen at random is a reasonable, if rough, representation. We refer to this type of operation as "blind-random" canvassing. The per-dollar productivity of such a canvass is a weighted average of the blind-canvass productivities in each precinct, the weights being the relative sizes of the precincts.

A more complicated but presumably more efficient mode of operation is where all canvassing is done blindly, but the precincts to be canvassed are chosen optimally. The Democratic canvass conducted in Los Angeles County in the 1962 California gubernatorial campaign may have approximated this pattern.[9] To choose optimally we compute the blind canvass productivities $\rho_1/c_1$ for each and arrange the precincts in that order until the budget is exhausted, or until the productivities become negative, whichever occurs first. We shall refer to this as a "blind-optimal" canvass.

Still another mode of operation is always to canvass selectively, but in precincts chosen at random. The average productivity is a weighted average of each of the selective-canvass productivities, the weights being the fraction of all registered A-partisans belonging to each precinct. We refer to this type of operation as a "selective-random" canvass.

Finally, we have a "selective-optimal" canvass, in which we canvass selectively in the most productive precincts. To select the most productive precinct, we rank them according to their selective-canvass productivities $\rho_2/c_2$ and then invest in the precincts in that order, until the budget is exhausted.

To recapitulate, in planning a canvass we must decide which precincts to canvass, and which tactic to use in those precincts. If the blind tactic is to be used everywhere, then we have either a blind-optimal or a blind-random canvass according to whether we attempt to choose the most productive precincts or not; if the selective tactic is to be used throughout, then we have either a selective-optimal or selective-random canvass, again depending upon whether the choice of precincts is optimized or not. Finally, full optimization resembles blind or selective optimization in attempting to optimize the choice of precincts, but it differs from both in that it does not require the same tactic to be used everywhere.

4.4   In order to compare these modes of operation we will apply each to the constituency described in Table 4.1. The data are

[9] See Helen Fuller, "The Man to See in California," *Harper's Magazine,* CCXXVI (January, 1963), 64 ff.

imaginary; however, they were chosen so as to present a plausible range of precinct types, and also (by setting $P_A > .5$ in most precincts) so as to make blind canvassing reasonably productive.

| Precinct | $P_A$ | $P_R$ | $P_V$ | N |
|---|---|---|---|---|
| 1 | .9 | .9 | .8 | 1000 |
| 2 | .9 | .9 | .6 | 1000 |
| 3 | .9 | .7 | .8 | 1000 |
| 4 | .9 | .7 | .6 | 1000 |
| 5 | .7 | .9 | .8 | 1000 |
| 6 | .7 | .9 | .6 | 1000 |
| 7 | .7 | .7 | .8 | 1000 |
| 8 | .7 | .7 | .6 | 1000 |
| 9 | .4 | .9 | .8 | 1000 |
| 10 | .4 | .9 | .6 | 1000 |
| 11 | .4 | .7 | .8 | 1000 |
| 12 | .4 | .7 | .6 | 1000 |

TABLE 4.1

We assume that blind canvassing costs ten cents per contact (which is probably a realistic, though rough, figure), and that selective canvassing costs twenty cents per contact (which is a guess). To apply the algorithm it is necessary to obtain the slopes $a_{i1}$, $a_{i2}$ of the two line segments of the concave approximations. From the expressions (4.1), (4.2) we can calculate the gains $G_1$, $G_2$ of saturating any precinct with each tactic, and similarly we can calculate the costs $C_1$, $C_2$ of doing so. These quantities are tabulated in columns (2) to (5) of Table 4.2. The productivity of the blind tactic is then $\dfrac{\rho_1}{c_1} = \dfrac{G_1}{C_1}$; of the selective tactic, $\dfrac{\rho_2}{c_2} = \dfrac{G_2}{C_2}$; and of the transition, from blind to selective saturation, $\dfrac{G_2 - G_1}{C_2 - C_1}$. These quantities are tabulated in columns (6), (7) and (8) of Table 4.2.

The slope $a_{i1}$ of the initial portion of the payoff function $f_i'$ of precinct i is given by the larger of $\rho_1/c_1$, $\rho_2/c_2$, as indicated in columns (6) and (7) of the table; if the larger is the blind-canvass productivity $\rho_1/c_1$, there is a second slope $a_{i2}$, given in column 8. To obtain an efficient canvass we invest to saturation in order of decreasing productivity (i.e., decreasing $a_{ij}$). The most productive opportunity (with a productivity of 1.15 votes per dollar) is a blind canvass in precinct 2; thus we first allocate $100 to saturate that precinct with a blind canvass. We then allocate $100 to the second most productive opportunity (.9 votes/dollar), a blind canvass in precinct 4; then $126 to saturate precinct 6 (or 8, 10, or 12, which are equally productive) with a selective canvass, and so on until the budget is exhausted. If the budget is large enough, the final allocation will be to the least productive opportunity, a switch from blind to selective saturation of precinct 1, which costs $62 and produces only .12 votes per dollar spent, for a total of 7.4 additional votes. To determine the overall gain we sum the gains produced by each expenditure; thus a budget of $100 produces 115 votes, $200 produces 205 votes, $326 produces 306 votes, and so on.

| | Blind | | Selective | | $\dfrac{G_1}{C_1}$ | $\dfrac{G_2}{C_2}$ | $\dfrac{G_2 - G_1}{C_2 - C_1}$ |
|---|---|---|---|---|---|---|---|
| | $G_1$ | $C_1$ | $G_2$ | $C_2$ | | | |
| Precinct | (Votes) | ($) | (Votes) | ($) | (V/$) | (V/$) | (V/$) |
| (1) | (2) | (3) | (4) | (5) | (6) | (7) | (8) |
| 1 | 58 | 100 | 65 | 162 | $.58 = a_{11}$ | .40 | $.12 = a_{12}$ |
| 2 | 115 | 100 | 130 | 162 | $1.15 = a_{21}$ | .80 | $.23 = a_{22}$ |
| 3 | 45 | 100 | 50 | 126 | $.45 = a_{31}$ | .40 | $.22 = a_{32}$ |
| 4 | 90 | 100 | 101 | 126 | $.90 = a_{41}$ | .80 | $.43 = a_{42}$ |
| 5 | 29 | 100 | 50 | 126 | .29 | $.40 = a_{51}$ | — |
| 6 | 58 | 100 | 101 | 126 | .58 | $.80 = a_{61}$ | — |
| 7 | 22 | 100 | 39 | 98 | .22 | $.40 = a_{71}$ | — |
| 8 | 45 | 100 | 78 | 98 | .45 | $.80 = a_{81}$ | — |
| 9 | −15 | 100 | 29 | 72 | −.15 | $.40 = a_{91}$ | — |
| 10 | −30 | 100 | 58 | 72 | −.30 | $.80 = a_{10,1}$ | — |
| 11 | −11 | 100 | 22 | 56 | −.11 | $.40 = a_{11,1}$ | — |
| 12 | −22 | 100 | 45 | 56 | −.22 | $.80 = a_{12,1}$ | — |

TABLE 4.2

In the blind-optimal type of canvass, we optimize only with respect to the blind-canvass productivities in column (6); thus we invest in precincts 2 (115 votes), 4 (205 votes), 6 (263 votes), etc. The final allocation, at an expenditure level of $800, is to precinct 7; even if the budget is larger we never allocate funds to the remaining precincts 9 through 12, since the results would be counterproductive. A selective-optimal canvass is handled similarly, using the selective-canvass productivities in column (7).

To obtain the per-dollar productivities for blind-random and selective-random canvasses we average the productivities in columns (6) and (7); the results are .32 votes per dollar (for budgets ≤ $1200) and .60 votes per dollar (for budgets ≤ $1280) respectively.

To get a general picture of how these modes of operation compare in efficiency we have plotted in Figure 4.2 the expected plurality gain produced by each, for budgets up to $1280.[10]

**FIGURE 4.2**

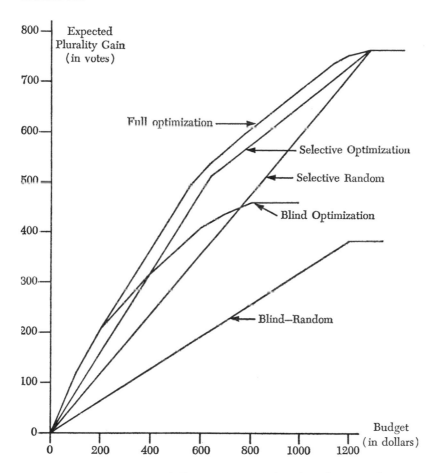

As we would expect, full optimization (F-0) is best, and con-

<hr>

[10] The "Full Optimization" plot is based, for convenience, on the concave approximations f' rather than the true yields f.

versely, the blind-random canvass is uniformly the least efficient. If for some reason only the blind tactic is possible, then clearly optimization (the B-0 mode) is worthwhile. Except at very large budgets the same is also true of the selective tactic; as the budget approaches $1,280, however, the S-0 and S-R modes (and the F-0 mode as well) become identical, since in all cases the recommended field activity—a selective canvass of the entire constituency—is the same. At small budget levels, blind optimization is superior to either type of selective canvass, and it is better than selective-random canvassing even at fairly large levels. However, this is in part an artifact of our example; in constituencies not so overwhelmingly pro-A in partisanship, B-0 canvassing could be inferior to S-0 or even S-R canvassing at every budget level. In such constituencies the relative advantage of F-0 over S-0 would also decrease, since use of the blind tactic—which is the only difference between F-0 and S-0—would be less attractive. The margin between S-0 and S-R would remain, since it depends basically on the heterogeneity of the constituency, rather than its partisanship; and the advantage of B-0 over B-R would grow, since in a balanced constituency blind-random canvassing would be unproductive or even counterproductive.

5.1 The analysis of the preceding sections has been based on a specific model of canvassing. Like any model, ours is a drastically simplified representation of a very complex and uncertain process. In empirical research of this kind, the investigator is always faced with a fundamental choice: whether to adopt a simple and therefore useful model, at the risk of being too simple and hence unrealistic; or whether, on the other hand, to employ a more complicated but more realistic model, which may prove to be too complex to be of much practical use. In the present study we chose a simple model, and as a result the analysis has been relatively straightforward. Before accepting it, however, it is important to consider the extent to which our conclusions are sensitive to possible violations of the assumptions on which the analysis is based. For example, we have assumed that certain information is available for planning purposes, and that this information is perfectly reliable; but what if it is not available, or not reliable? Also, a peculiarity of the campaign problem (which it shares with many military problems) is that it is a game situation, in which whatever strategy we select will be confronted by our opponent's counterstrategy. What happens to our analysis if, for example, our opponent conducts a canvass of his own? Let us briefly consider some of these possibilities.

5.2 We have so far assumed that we are able to make accurate forecasts of turnout levels, of the party's share of the vote in each precinct, and of the partisanship of individual voters. On the basis of these forecasts we can predict the effects of alternative allocations of our canvassing resources, and can therefore identify that allocation which is best. How sensitive are our conclusions to inaccuracies in these forecasts?

First consider the turnout predictions. Clearly certain combinations of errors could throw our calculations seriously awry; for example, if errors were concentrated in those precincts for which one tactic was best, then the effects and the relative efficiencies of the various modes of operation could be greatly altered. Such malevolent errors are always possible, but other types of error are more likely and are therefore of more interest. Forecast errors might be randomly and independently distributed across all precincts; provided they are not too large, the analysis is not substantially affected. A more important type of turnout-forecast error is where all precincts are affected comparably; for example, good or bad weather might cause all turnout rates to be generally above or below the forecasts. Suppose that the actual nonvoting rates $1 - P_V'$ are $\beta$ times the predicted rates (where $\beta > 1$ for bad weather, $\beta < 1$ for good weather). By inspection of (3.4) and (3.5), it is clear that using either tactic will yield $\beta$ times the predicted gain, and thus their relative (but not absolute) efficiencies are unaffected.

Now consider the partisanship forecasts; let us suppose that our information is unreliable, in the sense that only a certain fraction $\beta < 1$ of the voters actually do vote as predicted, the remainder voting for the opposition. If $P_A'$ is the forecast value, then the actual value of $P_A$, taking account of defection from and to party A, is evidently

$$P_A = \beta P_A' + (1 - \beta)(1 - P_A')$$
$$= P_A'(2\beta - 1) + (1 - \beta)$$

The blind-canvass productivity (3.3) contains a $(2P_A - 1)$ term which becomes, in terms of the forecast value,

$$2[P_A'(2\beta - 1) + 1 - \beta] - 1 = 2P_A'(2\beta - 1) + 2 - 2\beta - 1$$
$$= (2P_A' - 1)(2\beta - 1)$$

Hence the true blind-canvass will be $(2\beta - 1)$ times the forecast value. In a selective canvass the defection from A causes it in effect to become a blind canvass with productivity

$$\alpha(1 - P_V)(2\beta - 1), \tag{5.1}$$

which again is $(2\beta - 1)$ times the forecast productivity (3.5). Thus both tactics are again affected identically, and their relative efficiencies are unaffected.

A more pessimistic assumption (for A) is to suppose that defection takes place exclusively from A to B, and not in the opposite direction. If only $\beta$ of the forecast A-voters actually do vote for A, then the selective canvass productivity is again as in (5.1); the blind-canvass productivity, on the other hand, becomes

$$(2\beta P_A' - 1)(1 - P_V)P_R.$$

Thus the tactics are affected differently. To see what this means for our various canvassing modes, let us consider \$600 canvasses of each type; the forecast and actual effects of each type of canvass, conducted in the constituency described earlier, are tabulated in Table 5.1 for $\beta = .8$.

| Type of Canvass | % Defection: | |
| --- | --- | --- |
|  | 0% | 20% |
| F-0 | 513 votes | 286 votes |
| S-0 | 480 | 288 |
| B-0 | 410 | 200 |
| S-R | 360 | 216 |
| B-R | 192 | 62 |

TABLE 5.1

All modes are adversely affected by the defection, but the blind canvasses B-0, B-R are most seriously hurt. Conversely, had defection from B to A occurred, these modes would have taken greater advantage of the fact.) Although the selective tactic requires more detailed information than does the blind-canvassing tactic, nevertheless the modes which use this tactic (S-0, S-R) are not more sensitive, and in Table 5.1 are less sensitive, to various kinds of error in the information. However, these modes are affected seriously if the required information is simply unavailable. If only some of the supporters of A are individually known to the party, then the various modes will be affected as shown in Table 5.2 (again for budgets of \$600).

| Type of | | % of Supporters Known: | |
| Canvass | 100% | 75% | 50% |
| --- | --- | --- | --- |
| S-0 | 480 votes | 432 votes | 368 votes |
| B-0 | 410 | 410 | 410 |
| S-R | 360 | 360 | 360 |
| B-R | 192 | 192 | 192 |

TABLE 5.2

For the range of contingencies considered on the table, only the S-0 mode is affected; when fewer than 66% of the A-voters are known, the B-0 mode is better. If only 25% were known, then the S-R mode could produce no more than 192 votes, the same as the B-R gain; however, the cost would be much less, since a budget of $320 would then suffice to contact all known A-supporters. Full optimization, though not tabulated in the table, would be superior throughout, since the algorithm (with minor modification) takes account of information constraints by making more use of the blind tactic where necessary; in the limiting case where no supporters are known, full optimization becomes identical to blind optimization.

Another assumption which has been implicit throughout is that the opposition does not conduct a canvass of his own. Let us very briefly consider the consequences of relaxing this assumption. First suppose that the opposition contacts $\beta$ of all voters, at random. Then evidently $\beta$ of A's contacts are in effect wasted, since those voters have already been (or will be) contacted, and by our assumptions a second contact has no additional effect. Thus all tactics and all modes are affected similarly, and the relative efficiencies are unchanged.

The effects of an opposition selective canvass (at random) are more interesting. Such opposition activity will not affect a selective canvass by party A, since both parties contact only their own known supporters. If A conducts a blind canvass, then none of the contacts with A-supporters are wasted; on the other hand, $\beta$ of the contacts with B-voters are. Thus the blind canvass inspires fewer additional B-voters to vote, and therefore, oddly, becomes *more* productive; the actual per-contact productivity is

$$\alpha[P_A - (1 - \beta)(1 - P_A)](1 - P_V)P_R$$

When $\beta$ approaches unity (i.e., when the opposition contacts all the B-voters), then a blind A-canvass acts almost like a selective canvass, except that some contacts are still wasted on unregistered voters. Table 5.3 shows the effects of opposition selective canvassing upon the different kinds of $600 A-canvasses.

| Type of Canvass | % of B-voters contacted by opposition: | | |
|---|---|---|---|
| | 0% | 50% | 100% |
| F-0 | 513 votes | 528 votes | 545 votes |
| S-0 | 480 | 480 | 480 |
| B-0 | 410 | 467 | 529 |
| S-R | 360 | 360 | 360 |
| B-R | 192 | 288 | 384 |

TABLE 5.3

Even when the opposition canvasses half of its supporters the efficiency ranking is unchanged; however, with a 100% canvass, B-0 surpasses S-0 and B-R is better than S-R. Full optimization remains the most efficient mode throughout.

6.1 In the preceding three sections, we have suggested a simple and general method for planning a political canvass, which seems to offer advantages over various simpler approaches to the problem, and whose superiority in this respect does not seem to be highly sensitive to the specific assumptions on which our analysis was based. Whatever the practical relevance of these findings, the same method should be equally applicable to the very similar problems of telephone and mail canvassing. The same general approach, though with differences in detail, could be used to analyze the problems of planning a precampaign, partisan registration drive.

Clearly there are other campaign activities—television activities, for example—which are of a wholly different order of complexity. Even there, however, there is reason to hope that systematic quantitative analysis may become feasible in the not too distant future; operational research on marketing problems, for example, may lead to results of direct relevance to television campaigning.[11] In any event, the use of quantitative methods for policy analysis has proved to be fruitful in many different fields, and these methods deserve to be more widely known, and used, in political science.

---

[11] See, for example, J. D. Herniter and R. A. Howard, "Stochastic Marketing Models," chap. iii of Hertz and Eddison, *op. cit.*, pp. 33 ff.

# 4. Models of the Political System

# 4. Models of the Political System

## Introductory Note

*We are entering upon an age of reconstruction, in religion, in science, and in political thought. Such ages, if they are to avoid mere ignorant oscillation between extremes, must seek truth in its ultimate depths. There can be no vision of this depth of truth apart from a philosophy which takes full account of those ultimate abstractions, whose interconnections it is the business of mathematics to explore.*

*Alfred North Whitehead*

Although Plato believed in mathematics as the key to ultimate philosophical truth, he used verbal means to express his models of the political system. The mode of expression remained verbal for twenty-three hundred years, and only recently have scholars begun to convert to mathematical expression. The process of conversion has contributed a new rigor to political models. When the scholar attempts to translate his ideas into the language of mathematics, verbal ambiguities are discovered and must be eliminated. Vague ideas must be clarified and reduced to precision, if they are to be expressed in mathematical symbols. When this occurs, the scholar better understands his subject.[1]

Whether verbal or mathematical, model-building requires simplifying assumptions because all variables cannot be identified or controlled. This necessity of simplification is found in models of the physical, as well as the social, sciences. Any doubt that this is true is quickly dispelled when one contemplates what has happened to the Newtonian models in twentieth-century physics. In physics, as in other realms, mathematical models are merely abstractions, designed to approximate the real world. Despite their imperfections they have been useful to technology, as well as to science. Social scientists have the additional problem of the human psyche, which gives rise to a considerable variety of behaviors. Political scientists have, however, a source of comfort. The psychic problem has not caused psychiatrists and sociologists to despair, although their disciplines are, in some ways, less amenable to precise conceptualization than is political science.

---

[1] Otto A. Davis, "Final Critique of the Conference on Mathematical Application in Political Science," Southern Methodist University, Dallas, August 6, 1965.

Simplifying assumptions have been well-recognized limitations on scientific model-building. In his perceptive coupling of some modern political theories with some classical theories, William T. Bluhm describes Anthony Downs[2] and William H. Riker as "strategy theorists," and he compares their method with that of Hobbes. He quotes Chapter VII of *The Leviathan:*

> No discourse whatsoever can end in absolute knowledge of fact, past or to come. For as for the knowledge of fact, it is originally sense, and ever after memory. And for the knowledge of consequence, which I have said before is called science, it is not absolute but conditional. No man can know by discourse that this or that is, has been, or will be, which is to know absolutely, but only that if this be, that is; if this has been, that has been; if this shall be, that shall be—which is to know conditionally, and that not the consequence of one thing to another, but of one name of a thing to another name of the same thing.

Bluhm observes that even though the [conditional] knowledge we have always remains knowledge of an abstract world, not a real one,

> . . . if we are good at fitting the right "general names" to the particular "fancies" that inhibit our psyches, and if the rules we establish correspond to empirical laws, our scientific knowledge provides us with a powerful instrument of prediction and control over the world of sensible particulars. We can interpret the real world in the light of the model, and thus establish power over it. . . .
>
> [Hobbes asserts] that the theoretical reason is not a device for understanding and contemplating eternal objects, but an instrument for manipulating the world of sense, because the world of sense has a logical structure to it, susceptible of being known under the categories of a model world of "general names."[3]

*Riker's article on the size principle* is a postscript to his important volume, *The Theory of Political Coalitions,* in which the size principle is the central idea. Riker has undertaken no less than the "creation of a theoretical construct that is a somewhat simplified version of what the real world [of political coalitions] . . . is believed to be like." He suggests that propositions from his model can be validated or refuted empirically, and the model in consequence can be perfected or abandoned.

---

[2] *An Economic Theory of Democracy* (New York: Harper & Row, 1957).

[3] *Theories of the Political System* (Englewood Cliffs, N.J.: Prentice-Hall: 1965), pp. 267-270.

Game theory provides the conceptual basis for the model. The coalition theory includes these notions: an "n-person" game (more than two competitors), "zero sum" (gains precisely equal losses), rationality of the players. Riker's "irrefutable tautology," following Luce and Raiffa, states:

> Given a social situation in which exist two alternative courses of action leading to different outcomes and assuming that participants can order these outcomes on a subjective scale of preference, each participant will choose the alternative leading to the more preferred outcome.[4]

Assuming that "side payments" are permitted, Riker concludes that winning coalitions tend toward the absolute minimum size necessary for success. He also posits that a long-range result of competition in a political system, which includes these characteristics, is the elimination of participants. Consequently disequilibrium rather than a "balance of power" occurs.

Riker's work has been criticized on the ground that its simplifying assumptions, particularly the zero-sum assumption, make it inapplicable to real world politics. The author, however, anticipates this stricture with a variety of historical evidence to buttress his theory and a perceptive analysis devoted to the question of zero-sum applicability:

> . . . whether or not one should use the zero-sum model depends entirely on the way one's subject is commonly perceived. In discussing bargains, which are perceived as mutual gain, of course, a non-zero-sum model is probably best. On the other hand, in discussing elections and wars, which are perceived as requiring indivisible victory, the zero-sum model is probably best. . . .[5]

*The article by Otto A. Davis and Melvin Hinich* belongs to the same genre as the works of Riker and of Anthony Downs. There are the simplifying assumptions: Candidates have complete information about voter preferences regarding issues, and voters have complete information about candidate positions on all issues. These respective attitudes are formed and made known prior to nomination and election and are assumed to be unchanging. Each voter bases his electoral decision on a rational consideration: he

---

[4] *The Theory of Political Coalitions* (New Haven and London: Yale University Press, 1962, 1965), p. 18.

[5] *Ibid.*, p. 31.

supports the candidate whose position on the issues appears most likely to maximize his (the voter's) utility. Candidates, if elected, will adopt the policies announced prior to election. The model assumes that policies are measured by certain indices and that all voters use the same indices. Davis and Hinich demonstrate that, given these assumptions, including the known distribution of voters on a continuum, a median strategy normally wins over a non-median strategy.

The authors next consider the problem of a party nomination of a winning candidate. If a purely democratic nominating process is employed and if all voters in the system are members of a party in a two-party system, disequilibrium and resort to violence may occur, when a minority whose desires differ widely from the views of the majority are denied any chance of influencing policy.

If the policy position of a minority party candidate is preferred by enough members of the majority party to constitute a slight majority of all voters, the candidate of the minority party may win. Thus the model, in its application to the nomination problem, suggests that chances of victory in the general election may be improved by selection of a candidate whose position is a compromise between the desires of his own party members and the members of the other party.

The analysis reveals a *dilemma of nominations:* The democratic method of choosing a nominee permits rational party voters to seek maximization of their utilities by choosing a candidate whose position is harmonious with their own. The dictates of general election strategy, on the other hand, requires a compromise candidate who can appeal to some members of the opposition party. This kind of nomination may be achieved by abandoning democracy in favor of a "smoke-filled room" choice. The latter enables the party to choose a candidate whose position is more compatible with the entire population of voters (in both parties), although it may be less preferred by the subset of voters in the candidate's own party.

The reader will note that the Davis-Hinich model, although it analyzes "conditional" knowledge, describes and explains mathematically a number of observable uniformities which are found in party systems of the real world.

# A New Proof of the Size Principle

WILLIAM H. RIKER

*University of Rochester*

In *The Theory of Political Coalitions* I presented a proof of the size principle, which is an adaption to the world of real coalitions of the following inference from the theory of *n*-person games:

> In *n-person, zero-sum games, where side payments are permitted, where players are rational, and where they have perfect information, only minimum winning coalitions occur.*

The proof of this inference was, however, somewhat involved, so I take the opportunity of this paper to present a simpler and more easily understandable direct proof.

## I

As a preliminary step, let me recall for the reader some of the main notions of *n*-person game theory as set forth by Von Neumann and Morgenstern (2).

In two-person, zero-sum games, the problem faced by each player is the selection of a strategy (i.e., a complete set of choices for each possible move) such that the player receives an amount, v, which is the most he can unilaterally guarantee himself and the least his opponent can unilaterally hold him down to. In *n*-person games, however, the problem faced by each player, at least in all games where any kind of co-operation is permitted, is less a selection of strategy and more the selection of partners. Presumably two persons co-operating can sometimes accomplish more than both can acting individually. Hence the main action in *n*-person games is the formation of coalitions. Even though in the *n*-person case the problem of play is different from the problem of play in the two-person case, it is still possible to retain the notion of a value, v, which is the most that can be unilaterally guaranteed. Suppose a coalition, S, forms. Then the worst thing that can happen to it is that its complement, — S, forms. (That is, its complement, — S, can presumably give S more effective opposition than can smaller coalitions, P, Q, and R, where P ∪ Q ∪ R = — S.) If — S forms, we have something like a two-person game between S and — S and hence can speak of a value for S, v(S), which is called a characteristic function, and which is the amount S can guarantee itself regardless of what — S does

167

and also the amount $-$ S can hold S down to. The characteristic function is a real valued set function with the following properties:

(1) $v(\phi)=0$, where $\phi$ is the empty set. (Presumably an empty coalition is valueless.)

(2) $v(S) = -v(-S)$, which is the zero-sum condition.

(3) $v(I_n)=0$, where $I_n$ is the identity subset of the set, N, of players, that is, a coalition of the whole. (This property is an inference from (1) and (2).)

(4) $v(S \cup T) \geqslant v(S)+v(T)$, where S and T are disjoint subsets of N. When only the equality relation holds, the game is said to be *inessential* (for there is no point to making coalitions). Otherwise, the game is *essential*. In the subsequent discussion we will be concerned only with essential games.

An example of a characteristic function is:

$$\text{If S has } \begin{Bmatrix} 0 \\ 1 \\ 2 \\ 3 \\ 4 \\ 5 \end{Bmatrix} \text{ members, } v(S) = \begin{Bmatrix} 0 \\ -20 \\ -40 \\ 40 \\ 20 \\ 0 \end{Bmatrix}$$

In order to render characteristic functions in a form that allows easy comparison among games, it is customary to normalize them by letting the coalition a single player be worth a given minimum, say, $-\gamma$. That is,

(5) $v([i]) = -\gamma$

Setting $-\gamma = -1$, we have the following normalized form for the foregoing example:

$$\text{If S has } \begin{Bmatrix} 0 \\ 1 \\ 2 \\ 3 \\ 4 \\ 5 \end{Bmatrix} \text{ members, } v(S) = \begin{Bmatrix} 0 \\ -1 \\ -2 \\ 2 \\ 1 \\ 0 \end{Bmatrix}$$

Characteristic functions do not, however, completely describe an *n*-person game. What counts for the individual player is not just the value of the coalition, however much that may be, but rather what portion of the value he personally receives. It is conceivable that player *i*, whose individual receipts are denoted by the symbol "$a_i$," may prefer a coalition $S_2$ to a coalition $S_1$, where

$v(S_1)>v(S_2)$, if $a_i > a_j$. One must, therefore, describe not only
$$i \in S_2 \quad j \in S_1$$
the payoff to coalitions but also the payoff to individuals, which
latter are called imputations: An imputation is an n-tuple of real
numbers, $\alpha = (a_1, a_2, \ldots, a_n)$, which satisfies the following conditions:

(6) $a_i \geqslant v([i])$, which asserts that no player will accept in any
coalition an amount less than he can obtain in a coalition
of himself alone; and

(7) $\sum_{i=1}^{n} a_i = 0$, which is not only the zero-sum condition, but also
asserts that rational players, whatever their coalition
structure, will obtain the full value of the game.

## II

The task of $n$-person theory is to place some limitations on both
characteristic functions and imputations in order to render the outcomes predictable. Von Neumann and Morgenstern initiated this
process with a discussion of the range of characteristic functions.
Specifically, they showed:

(8) if S has 0 members, $v(S) = 0$          (from (1))
(9) if S has 1 member, $v(S) = -\gamma$.          (from (5))
(10) if S has $(n-1)$ members, $v(S) = \gamma$.          (from (2) and (5))
(11) if S has $n$ members, $v(S) = 0$.          (from (3))
(12) if S has $p$ members, where $2 \leqslant p \leqslant (n-2)$,
then $-p\gamma \leqslant v(S) \leqslant (n-p)\gamma$.          (from (6))

Graphically these results can be shown thus:

Figure 1

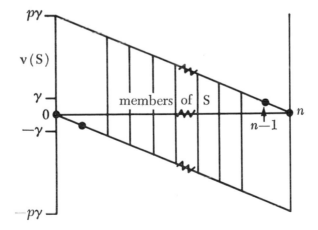

where points $(0,0)$, $(1, -\gamma)$, $((n-1),\gamma)$, and $(n,0)$ represent assertions (8), (9), (10), and (11) respectively and where the vertical lines represent assertion (12). Since Von Neumann and Morgenstern did not wish to use the notion of a majority (because they wished to allow for weighted players who, though fewer than a numerical majority, might win and because they wished to allow for discriminatory solutions in which some players were guaranteed minimum gains and losses), they could not narrow the range further. One can, however, use the notions either of a majority of equally weighted persons or of a majority of equal units of weight, thereby preserving the feature of weights while permitting much further narrowing of the range of characteristic functions. (Here we will be concerned only with majorities of equally weighted persons; but for a presentation of the majority notion in terms of units of weight, see reference (1), pp. 253-61.) In so doing, we are, of course, limiting ourselves to nondiscriminatory solutions for, if the notion of a majority is used, discrimination can appear only as unequal weighting.

Let $m$ be the minimal value of a majority, where

(13) $\left[ \dfrac{(n+1)}{2} \text{or } \left( \left( \dfrac{n}{2} \right) + 1 \right) \right] \leqslant m < n$. (Note that the right in-
equation is written "$m < n$" rather than "$m \leqslant n$," as is often customary. If $m = n$, there is nothing to do in the game except form the single coalition, $I_n$, of all players, which fact renders characteristic function theory trivial.)

The following definitions can now be offered

(14) if $p > n - p$ and $p \geqslant m$, then $S_p \in W$, where W is the set of all winning coalitions; if $S_p \in W$, then $v(S) \geqslant 0$; if $p \neq n$, then, for $S \in W$, $v(S) > 0$, which follows from (4) since we have assumed the game is essential.

(15) if $p = m$, then $S_p \in W^m$, where $W^m$ is the set of minimal winning coalitions such that $S_p - 1 \notin W^m$.

(16) if $(n-p) \leqslant p < m$, $S_p \in B$, where B is the set of blocking coalitions; and $v(S) = 0$.

(17) if $S \notin W$ and $S \notin B$, then $S \in L$, where L is the set of losing coalitions; $v(S) \leqslant 0$; if $p > 0$, then $v(S) < 0$, which follows from (2) and (14). With these definitions it is possible to rewrite (12), narrowing the range of $v(s)$:

(18) if $S \in W$, then $0 \leqslant v(S) \leqslant (n-p)\gamma$.        (from (12) and (14))

(19) if $S \in B$, then $v(S) = 0$.        (from (16))

(20) if $S \in L$, then $-p\gamma \leqslant v(S) \leqslant 0$.          (from (12) and (17))

Ignoring the possibility of blocking coalitions, the results can be shown graphically thus:

Figure 2

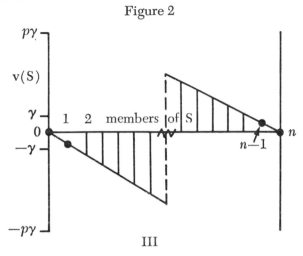

III

Even though the range of characteristic functions has thus been narrowed largely by eliminating discriminatory solutions, we still know relatively little about what coalitions might occur and about what imputations might be associated with them. In this section, I shall set forth another kind of restriction on coalitions which permits a prediction about the range of occurrenes and which is sometimes useful in political analysis.

We can assume, of course, that, since the game is essential, some $S$, $S \in W$, and some $-S$, $-S \in L$, occur (ignoring here the possibility of blocking coalitions). If, however, there exists some $S_q$, $S_q \in W$, and some imputation, $\alpha$, associated with $S_q$, such that $S_q$ can guarantee its members more than they might receive in a smaller coalition and at least as much as they might receive in a larger one, then they would prefer coalitions of size $q$ to all others. Such coalitions, $S_q$, are realizable, while all others $S_p$, where $p \neq q$, are unrealizable. Presumably, once a coalition reaches a realizable size, it is relatively stable, except of course for internal squabbles over the division of $v(S)$ into $a_i$.
$$\scriptstyle i \in S$$

The intuitive idea in the notion of realizable coalitions is that, in the set $W$, there is a subset of realizable coalitions, $W^q$, such that any coalition in $W^q$ is preferred to any coalition not in it because in S, $S \epsilon W^q$, the amounts that S can unilaterally (that is, without the co-operation of $-S$) guarantee its members individually are at a maximum and, for that maximum, the costs of organization are minimal.

Stating this notion formally: For $S_p$, $S_q$ and $S_r$, where $p < q < r$, $S_q$ is realizable if, for $S_q \epsilon W$, it is possible that

(I)  $a_i^{S_p} < a_i^{S_q}$; and

(II) $a_i^{S_q} \geq a_i^{S_r}$,

where the notation "$a_i^{S_x}$" means "the payment to $i$ when $i$ is a member of $S_x$" and $x = \{p,q,r\}$.

The theorem to be proved is: $W^q = W^m$. That is, only minimal winning coalitions are realizable. In the proof, I shall show, first, that S, $S \epsilon W^m$ fulfill condition (I), second, that they fulfill condition (II), and third, that they alone of all S, $S \epsilon W$, fulfill both conditions.

First, let there be two sets $S_p$ and $S_q$, where $p < m$, $q = m$, and $S_p$ is a proper subset of $S_q$. Here it is always true, by reason of (14), (17), (18), and (20), that $v(S_p) < v(S_q)$, for $v(S_p)$ is a negative number or zero while, when $q = m$, $v(S_q)$ is a positive one. Hence the amount $[v(S_q) - v(S_p)]$ can always be divided among the $i$, $i \epsilon S_p$ and $S_q$, and the $j$, $j \epsilon S_q$, $j \notin S_p$, in such a way as to guarantee that $a_i^{S_q} > 0$ and $a_i^{S_p} < a_i^{S_q}$. (That is, $S_p$, by turning itself into a minimal winning coalition, $S_q$, can increase its value sufficiently to pay all its old members more than they receive in $S_p$ and to pay its new members something for joining.) Hence S, $S \epsilon W^m$, satisfies Condition I of being realizable.

Second, let there be two sets $S_q$ and $S_r$, where $m = q < r$, and where $S_q$ is a proper subset of $S_r$. Here it is possible that $v(S_q) \gtreqless v(S_r)$. So it is necessary to prove that S, $S \epsilon W^m$, meets condition (II) in each of three cases:

Case 1. $v(S_q) > v(S_r)$. Since $v(S_q) > v(S_r)$, it is always possible to form $S_q$ in such a way that, for $i \epsilon S_q$ and $S_r$,

$$a_i^{S_q} = a_i^{S_r} + d_i \sum_{h \notin S_q} a_h^{S_r} + d_i [v(S_q) - v(S_r)]$$

where $\sum_{i \epsilon S_q} d_i = 1$ and $d_i > 0$. (That is, by reducing from $S_r$, the members of $S_q$ can keep what they get in $S_r$, divide up the payments made in $S_r$ to the people ejected when $S_q$ was formed, and divide up the increase in value.) Thus it is possible that $a_i^{S_q} > a_i^{S_r}$.

Case 2. $v(S_q) = v(S_r)$. As in case 1, it is possible to form $S_q$ so that, for $i \in S_q$ and $S_r$,

$$a_i^{Sq} = a_i^{Sr} + d_i \sum_{h \notin Sq} a_h^{Sr}.$$

Hence, as in Case 1, it is possible that $a_i^{Sq} > a_i^{Sr}$.

Case 3. $v(S_q) < v(S_r)$. In this case, there are three subcases according to the size of the sum of the payments to $h$, $h \in S_r$, $h \notin S_q$. It may be that $\sum_{h \notin Sq} a_h^{Sr} \gtreqless v(S_r) - v(S_q)$.

Case 3.1 $\sum_{h \notin Sq} a_h^{Sr} > v(S_r) - v(S_q)$. Since $[v(S_q) + \sum_{h \notin Sq} a_h^{Sr}] > v(S_r)$, it is possible to form $S_q$ in such a way that $a_i^{Sq} > a_i^{Sr}$, $i \in S_q$ and $S_r$. For example, if $a_i^{Sr} = d_i (v(S_r))$, then let $a_i^{Sq} = d_i [v(S_q) + \sum_{h \notin Sq} a_h^{Sr}]$.

Case 3.2 $\sum_{h \notin Sq} a_h^{Sr} = v(S_r) - v(S_q)$. By the condition of this case, that $[v(S_q + \sum_{h \notin Sq} a_h^{Sr}] = v(S_r)$, it is possible that $a_i$ be chosen so that at least $a_i^{Sq} = a_i^{Sr}$.

Case 3.3 $\sum_{h \notin Sq} a_h^{Sr} < v(S_r) - v(S_q)$. Let $b = v(S_r) - v(S_q) - \sum_{h \in Sq} a_h^{Sr}$. Then $b$ is the amount that all $i$, $i \in S_q$, might gain from enlarging the coalition $S_q$ to $S_r$. Let $c = v(S_r) - v(S_q)$. Then $c$ is the amount that $-S_r$ can afford to offer $h$, $h \in S_r$, $h \notin S_q$, to form $-S_q$. If $\sum_{h \notin Sq} a_h^{Sr} > 0$, then $c > b$. If $\sum_{h \notin Sq} a_h^{Sr} = 0$, then $c = b$. We can expect from assertion (7) that $-S_r$ will bid for $h$ up to the amount $c$, which will then bring about the situation in which $a_i^{Sr} - a_i^{Sq} = 0$. (Only a kind of altruistic good will on the part of $-S_r$ can prevent this result; and such good will is not to be expected in a zero-sum game.) Hence $a_i^{Sq} = a_i^{Sr}$. In this case it is argued that, if $S_r$ is formed, it is not realizable because $-S_r$ can by appropriate bidding force the formation of $S_q$, $S_q \in W^m$. Then there are the following discernible entities:

(1) $S_q$; (2) those members of $-S_q$ for which $a_i$ is a negative number; and (3) those members of $-S_q$ for which $a_i$ is a positive number or zero.

In sub-cases 3.2 and 3.3, $a_i^{Sq} = a_i^{Sr}$ and in sub-case 3.1 and Cases 1 and 2, $a_i^{Sq} > a_i^{Sr}$. Hence condition (II), that $a_i^{Sq} \geq a_i^{Sr}$ is fulfilled by $S$, $S \in W^m$.

Third, it remains to show that only $S$, $S \in W^m$ fulfill both conditions. Since in cases 1, 2, and 3.1 of the proof that $S$,

$S \in W^m$ fulfilled condition (II), it was shown that $a_i^{S_q}$ could satisfy the inequation $a_i^{S_q} > a_i^{S_r}$, and since it had already been established that $a_i^{S_q} > a_i^{S_p}$, it follows that in these cases, only $S$, $S \in W^m$ satisfies both conditions. But in cases 3.2 and 3.3 it was shown only that $a_i^{S_q} = a_i^{S_r}$. Since it is thus possible that, for some choice of $r$, $r \neq q$, $a_i^{S_r} \geq a_i^{S_{r+1}}$, both $S_r$ and $S_q$ are possible candidates for fulfilling condition (II). But since $a_i^{S_r} = a_i^{S_q}$, where $q < r$, clearly $S_r$ does not fulfill condition (I) which requires that $a_i^{S_r} > a_i^{S_q}$. But when $q = m$, $S_q$ does fulfill condition (I), even in cases 3.2 and 3.3. Hence only $S$, $S \in W^m$ fulfills both conditions simultaneously. Thus only minimal winning coalitions are realizable. That is, $W^q = W^m$.

## IV

The size principle does not by any means solve all the problems connected with $n$-person games. Since in a simple majority game where players are weighted equally, there are 1, 2,...., t possible coalitions in $W^q$, where $t = \binom{m}{n}$, it is apparent that the size principle does not narrow the selection down to a unique coalition. (As I have shown in (1), pp. 127-39, however, in some simple majority games where players are weighted unequally, $W^q$ is a single member set.) Furthermore, the size principle tells us very little about imputations, except that given some payoff to $i$ in $S_p$ or $S_r$, the payoff to $i$ in $S_q$ is equal to or better than the payoff in $S_p$ or $S_r$. Finally, since the narrowing that permitted the size principle eliminated games in which particular players are specially favored or disfavored, it tells us nothing about games in which discrimination is permitted. In short, there are many non-unique features of predictions in $n$-person theory. Nevertheless, as I tried to demonstrate in (1), the narrowing accomplished here permits some new and revealing interpretations of politics.

## REFERENCES

1. RIKER, WILLIAM H. *The Theory of Political Coalitions.* New Haven: Yale University Press, 1963.
2. VON NEUMANN, JOHN, and MORGENSTERN, OSKAR. *The Theory of Games and Economic Behavior.* 3d ed.; Princeton: Princeton University Press, 1947.

# A Mathematical Model of Policy Formation in a Democratic Society[1]

OTTO A. DAVIS and MELVIN HINICH

*Carnegie Institute of Technology*

## 1. *Introduction*

It is obvious that there are many factors which influence the policies adopted by a democratic government. Close observers of the political scene easily can cite instances where the very complexity of the governmental organization allows one part of that entity to have policies which serve to frustrate the policies of another part. It is equally clear that instances exist in our complex system where some policies of some parts of our government are unknown to our elected leaders (not to mention the people). There is no doubt but that any truly general and complete theory of policy formation should explain such anomalies. Nevertheless, they are ignored in the developments which follow. Instead of these anomalies, attention is centered on an idealized situation where full knowledge of governmental policy is available to all.

It is also evident that in a democracy where a government enjoys power because it won an election, that government's policies must bear some relationship to the desires of the voters. The determination of this relationship is the problem with which this paper is concerned. Nevertheless, it should be admitted at the outset that the very concept of the "desires of the voters" is somewhat ambiguous. Although it cannot be denied that some members of the population (and perhaps all of the relevant population for some subset of issues) have clearly defined positions on policy, evidence reported by various pollsters would seem to indicate that, at least for some issues, the very debate connected with an election may have an influence upon public opinion. Partly because such an influence does not seem to be fully understood, this phenomenon also is omitted from the model developed here. Perhaps the sole justification of this and the above omissions is that

[1] This research was supported by a grant from Resources for the Future to the Graduate School of Industrial Administration, Carnegie Institute of Technology. While only the authors are responsible for the contents of this paper, the comments of Morris DeGroot, Carnegie Institute of Technology, and Aaron Wildavsky, University of California at Berkeley, are gratefully acknowledged.

one must learn to walk before one is able to run. Yet, these omissions mean that this paper should be viewed as an effort to study only one idealized aspect of the real situation.

The particular (and main) problem investigated here is as follows: Given the precisely defined (see the developments below) and unchangeable preferences of the voters in the population, candidates for public office compete for votes by announcing before an election their exact position on each of the relevant issues. Each voter compares the positions taken by the various candidates and casts his vote for that particular candidate whose position is "nearest" (a more careful definition is given below) his own most preferred position. It is assumed that, once elected, a (former) candidate will adopt those policies which he announced during the campaign. Thus the questions to be answered are whether, and under what conditions, dominant strategies exist for the candidates.

Other problems also are analyzed within this context. For example, the policy choice of a beneficient dictator is compared with the dominant strategy for two candidates in a democratic system. The dilemma inherent in the process of nominating a candidate is discussed. Finally, a basic assumption is relaxed to allow for the possibility that one portion of the population may not care about some particular subset of issues while the other portion feels strongly about these very issues.

## 2. *Basic Assumptions and Tools of Analysis*

In order to be able to handle these basic problems, it is necessary to make some simplifying assumptions. First, it must be presumed that, at least conceptually, policies can be measured by certain indices. Consider, for example, the issue of civil rights. One might use several indices to measure the various characteristics of this issue. Voting rights might be measured by the percentage of the adult, nonwhite population which can be registered to vote. Integration in the schools and in housing might be measured by the variance of the percentages of nonwhites attending the various schools and living in the various localities respectively. Job discrimination might be measured by the percentage of nonwhites employed in various categories of work. On the other hand, one might use an index of these various indices. The crucial point is that some type of measurement be admitted.

Granted that policies can be measured by the postulated indices, another (even stronger) assumption is now appropriate. It is that each voter in the population uses the same indices to measure any given policy. In other words, the indices measuring the various policies are common to all voters. It is apparent that this assumption means that since the number of variables which measure any policy issue is somewhat arbitrary, all voters in the population are assumed to have the same given degree of sophistication in the manner in which they view policies.

It is assumed further that each voter has a preferred position for each issue of policy. This preferred position can be represented by certain values of the variables which measure each policy. Consequently, the $i^{th}$ voter's preferred position on all the issues of policy can be represented by the vector

$$x_i = [x_{i1}, x_{i2}, \ldots, x_{in}]'$$

where the components of the vector $x_i$ represent the desired values of the indices which measure the given policies.[2] Thus $x_{i1}$ might represent the percentage of the adult, nonwhite population which can be registered to vote; $x_{i2}$ and $x_{i3}$ might measure respectively the variance of the percentages of nonwhites attending the various schools and living in the various localities; etc.

In a manner similar to which the preferred position (or point) of an individual voter is represented, the vector

$$\theta_j = [\theta_{j1}, \theta_{j2}, \ldots, \theta_{jn}]'$$

can be taken to represent the position (or "platform") of the $j^{th}$ candidate. The column vector $\theta_j$ is presumed to be announced before any election and is known to all voters.

Since only in a degenerate case could $x_i = \theta_j$ for all i, some provision must be made for the "loss" which any voter feels when his preferred policy position is not the one selected for enactment. Such provision can be accomplished by the introduction of individual loss functions. Obviously, loss functions should exhibit certain intuitively desirable properties. Let $\theta$ represent governmental policy. Then $\theta$ is a vector composed of the indices discussed above. For the moment, view the components of $\theta$ as variables. Consider the $i^{th}$ voter. Obviously, if $x_i = \theta$, then this individual's loss should be zero since governmental policy is the same as his preferred position on all issues. However, consonant with the notion that each individual does have a preferred position for

---

[2] The prime (') on the explicit vector on the right hand side of the equality denotes the operation "transpose." Thus $x_1$ is a column vector.

each issue of policy, then if $x_i \neq \theta$ the $i^{th}$ voter should have a positive loss. These properties are present in the following specification of the $i^{th}$ voter's loss function:

$$(2.1) \quad L_i(\theta) = (x_i - \theta)'A(x_i - \theta)$$

where $L_i$ represents the loss function and A is a symmetric, positive definite matrix of rank n.[3]

Observe that (2.1) is a quadratic form. Obviously, the specification of this specific form requires further justification, since other functions possess the two properties discussed above. However, a quadratic form is the simplest of the class of functions having these properties and it is preferable, other things being equal, on this basis. Second, a loss function has an obvious relationship to the economist's notion of a utility function and, in fact, a quadratic loss function can be derived from a quadratic utility function. The basic notion underlying utility analysis is that of declining marginal utility. A quadratic utility function incorporates this concept. It follows that a quadratic loss function is acceptable on this basis. Third, it can be argued that no matter what the "true" loss function (at least if it incorporates the properties specified in the above paragraph), then a quadratic can serve as an acceptable approximation. This argument can be based upon expanding the function in a Taylor's series, noting that the first order terms are zero if the loss is symmetric, and throwing away the third and higher order terms. Finally, the authors argue that the proof of the pudding is in the eating and that intuitively interesting and informative results can be derived on the basis of quadratic losses.

For the special case of $n = 1$ (one issue with a single index) the loss function (2.1) is plotted in Figure 1. Note that it is symmetric around the point of zero loss ($x_i = \theta$).

It should be pointed out that the matrix A in (2.1) is not given a subscript. The reason for this omission is a rather strong assumption. Although the components of the vector $x_i$ can assume any values which the $i^{th}$ individual might desire, it is presumed that the tastes of the voters are such that the matrix A enters the loss function of each individual. The population of voters is assumed

---

[3] By definition, a $n \times n$ matrix A is symmetric if it is equal to its transpose; that is, if $A = A'$. The assumption that A is positive definite is a sufficient condition for the property $L_i(\theta) \geq 0$ for all $\theta$ and $L_i(\theta) = 0$ if and only if $x_i = \theta$. A necessary and sufficient condition for A to be positive definite is that the naturally ordered principal minors of A are all positive. See, e.g., G. Hadley, *Linear Algebra* (Reading: Addison-Wesley, 1961), pp. 251-63.

to have a certain "homogeneity." In other words, although voters desire differing values of the indices of policy, all voters assign the same relative "weight" (or "importance") to any given issue.[4] This (admittedly unrealistic) presumption is made solely for the reason of analytical convenience. It should be noted, on the other hand, that since utility losses are highly personal matters with no inter-individual scale of measurement which has meaning, care must be exercised in attaching any significance to a comparison of the numerical values of the losses of any two given individuals. However, the very notion that utility functions are unique only up to a monotonic transformation provides a (somewhat weak) rationalization to the assumption that the matrix A enters the loss of function of each individual. At least for a class of loss functions, suitable transformations could be performed on these functions so that this assumption could be satisfied.

Finally, there is the problem of characterizing the population of voters. Granted the previous assumptions, this can be accomplished by presuming that the preferred positions of all voters have been plotted into an n dimensional frequency and that this frequency has been suitable normalized into a density $f(x)$. While this density is naturally discrete, for the most part it will be approximated by a continuous density. It should be noted that this method of characterizing the population gives one access to the tools of probability theory for the purpose of analysis.

As a matter of notation, it is presumed that

(2.2)  $Ex = \delta$

where E represents the operation of taking expected values so that $\delta$ is the vector whose components are the means of the components of the $x_i$. Also,

(2.3)  $E(x - \delta)(x - \delta)' = \Sigma$

where $\Sigma$ is an $n \times n$ matrix whose diagonal elements are variances and non-diagonal elements are covariances.

It is convenient to introduce the notion of the norm. Let z represent an n component vector. The norm of the vector z with respect to the matrix A is defined as follows:

(2.4)  $\| z \| = \sqrt{z'Az}$

The norm represents the "length" of the vector z. Since A is positive definite, then $z \neq 0$ implies $\| z \| > 0$. The norm also repre-

---

[4] See, however, the discussion of Section 6 where this assumption is modified slightly.

sents the "distance" between two vectors. For example, the norm

$$(2.5) \quad \| z_1 - z_2 \| = \sqrt{(z_1 - z_2)'A(z_1 - z_2)}$$

represents the "distance" between vectors $z_1$ and $z_2$ with respect to the matrix A. In the developments below, a norm with respect to the matrix A⫫A is used also. This norm is distinguished by the notation

$$(2.6) \quad \| z \|^* = \sqrt{z'A⫫Az}$$

### 3. Two Candidates and a Beneficent Dictatorship

It is convenient and appropriate, before analyzing the basic case of electoral competition between two candidates, to consider the policies which a wise and beneficent dictator might choose. In this way, the dictator's choice can be compared with the policies resulting from the competition of the democratic process.

First of all, it is clear that the dictator must make some assignment of the weights of the importance (to the dictator) of the losses suffered by the various individuals in the population. Suppose that the dictator decides to weigh all individuals equally and makes the value judgment that utility losses are interpersonally comparable. Thus he decides that his policies should be chosen so that the average loss is minimized. In other words, the dictator desires to choose a vector $\theta$ such that the expression

$$(3.1) \quad E(x - \theta)'A(x - \theta) = E \| x - \theta \|^2 = \text{tr} ⫫A + \| \theta - \delta \|^2$$

is minimized.[5] It is clear that this expression is at a minimum when $\theta$ is chosen such that $\theta = \delta$. In other words, granted the dictator's value judgment, and also granted his desire to minimize that quantity which he perceives to be the total of the utility losses in the population, he must choose his policies to be the average of the preferred positions of the individuals in the population.

Turning now to the case of two-candidate competition in a democratic society, it is convenient to begin by stating that the candidates will be called "one" ant "two" respectively so that $\theta_1$ denotes the platform of the 1st candidate and $\theta_2$ represents the platform of the 2nd candidate. These platforms are announced be-

---

[5] In this notation, $(x-\theta)'A(x-\theta) = \| x-\theta \|^2$ by definition. In other words, the quantities are the same except for notation. Thus $\| \theta-\delta \|^2 = (\theta-\delta)'A(\theta-\delta)$. The trace of a matrix (denoted "tr" above) is defined as follows: Let B represent an $n \times n$ matrix whose elements are denoted $b_{ij}$. Then

$$\text{tr } B = \sum_{i=1}^{n} b_{ii}.$$

In other words, the trace of B is the sum of the diagonal elements.

fore the election day and form the basis for the voters' choices between the two candidates. (Recall the convenient assumption that the elected candidate will honor his platform.) Essentially, a voter is assumed to choose that candidate whose platform gives the smallest utility loss. In other words, the $i^{th}$ voter will cast his ballot for the $1^{st}$ candidate if

$$(3.2) \quad (x_i - \theta_1)'A(x_i - \theta_1) < (x_i - \theta_2)'A(x_i - \theta_2)$$

and it obviously follows that if

$$(3.3) \quad (x_i - \theta_1)'A(x_i - \theta_1) > (x_i - \theta_2)'A(x_i - \theta_2)$$

the $2^{nd}$ candidate will receive the $i^{th}$ individual's vote. In the unlikely event that the utility losses are the same, it can be presumed that the voter makes his choice by flipping a fair coin.

Having developed the rules for a voter's choice of candidates, it is appropriate to consider the relationship between this analysis and the works of Hotelling,[6] Downs,[7] and Tullock.[8] The unifying elements in the relevant parts of these works are two presumptions. First, there is only one index of policy. Second, distance can be used to determine how a voter will cast his ballot. Thus in the terminology of this analysis, let $n=1$. Then a representative loss function is presented in Figure 1. Given the previous assumptions, this function must be symmetric. It follows that (3.2) obtains if and only if $|x_i - \theta_1| < |x_i - \theta_2|$ and (3.3) obtains if and only if $|x_i - \theta_1| > |x_i - \theta_2|$. In other words, a voter chooses that candidate whose platform is nearest to his own (the voter's) preferred position.[9]

Consider the number $\theta^*$ which satisfies the following conditions:

$$P(x \leqslant \theta^*) \leqslant \tfrac{1}{2}$$

(3.4)

$$P(x \geqslant \theta^*) \geqslant \tfrac{1}{2}$$

where P represents "probability." In other words, $\theta^*$ is the (not necessarily unique) median of $f(x)$.

Consider now the problem of the choice of platforms. Suppose that the $1^{st}$ candidate selects the platform $\theta_1 = \theta^*$ and the $2^{nd}$ candidate selects some platform $\theta_2 \neq \theta^*$ where $\theta^*$ represents any

---

[6] Harold Hotelling, "Stability in Competition," *Economic Journal*, XXXIX (1929), 41-57; reprinted in G. J. Stigler and K. E. Boulding (eds.), *Readings in Price Theory* (Chicago: Richard D. Irwin, 1952), pp. 467-484.

[7] Anthony Downs, *An Economic Theory of Democracy* (New York: Harper, 1957).

[8] Gordon Tullock, *The Politics of Bureaucracy* (Washington: Public Affairs Press, 1965).

[9] The notation|.| denotes "absolute value." In a single dimension, this is a measure of distance.

number which satisfies (3.4). Put another way, the 1st candidate chooses a median strategy while the 2nd candidate selects a non-median platform. Given these choices, it is clear that (under the assumptions) the 1st candidate will win the election. In other words, the median is a dominant strategy. A choice of the median insures a candidate of at least an even chance of winning.

In order to justify this theorem, it is sufficient to observe that the very definition of the median (3.4) insures the 1st candidate of having a platform nearer to the preferred positions of at least one-half of the voters than the platform of the 2nd candidate. This fact is also obvious in Figure 2 where a density $f(x)$ is drawn, $\theta^*$ represents the median, and $\theta_2 \neq \theta^*$ is an arbitrary choice of the other candidate.

Given the presumed voting rules (3.2 and 3.3), it is clear that the best that the 2nd candidate can do is also to select a median strategy $\theta_2 = \theta^*$. In this event both candidates have an even chance of winning.

The dominance of the strategy of playing the median means that insofar as candidates are interested in winning the election, they should try to achieve this "middle position." Non-median strategies are to be avoided, for they only invite defeat. (At least under the assumptions made here, which implicitly include the presumption that all qualified individuals vote.)

Contrast this result with the presumed choice of a beneficent dictator. When the density $f(x)$ of preferred points is such that the mean and median coincide, then the dominant strategy for a candidate is the same as the beneficent dictator's choice. However, if the density $f(x)$ is skewed so that the mean and median are not the same, then the choices differ.

The question arises as to whether this result can be extended. It is particularly interesting to inquire as to whether anything can be said when the number of components in the vector x is greater than one. In this regard, let $n > 1$ be an arbitrary integer. This means that $f(x)$ is a multivariate density. It is necessary to perform a certain amount of algebraic manipulation to get the voting rules into a form which is useful for analysis.

Consider the instance in which the $i^{th}$ individual votes for the 1st candidate so that (3.2) is presumed to obtain. Dropping the i subscripts for convenience, it is easily seen that (3.2) can be expanded into the following equivalent statement

(3.5) $\quad x'Ax - 2x'A\theta_1 + \theta_1'A\theta_1 < x'Ax - 2x'A\theta_2 + \theta_2'A\theta_2$

since $x'A\theta_1 = \theta_1'Ax$ and $x'A\theta_2 = \theta_2'Ax$. By taking $\theta_2'A\theta_2$ to the left hand side and $2x'A\theta_1$ to the right hand side, the expression

(3.6) $\theta_1'A\theta_1 - \theta_2'A\theta_2 < 2x'A(\theta_1 - \theta_2)$

is obtained. This can be written as

(3.7) $(\theta_1 + \theta_2)'A(\theta_1 - \theta_2) < 2x'A(\theta_1 - \theta_2)$

and by subtracting $2\delta'A(\theta_1 - \theta_2)$ from both sides, the expression

(3.8) $(\theta_1 + \theta_2)'A(\theta_1 - \theta_2) - 2\delta'A(\theta_1 - \theta_2) <$
$$2(x - \delta)'A(\theta_1 - \theta_2)$$

is obtained. Examine the left hand side of this expression (3.8). The following is simply an algebraic manipulation.

(3.9) $(\theta_1 + \theta_2)'A(\theta_1 - \theta_2) - 2\delta'A(\theta_1 - \theta_2) =$
$(\theta_1 + \theta_2 - 2\delta)'A(\theta_1 - \theta_2) = [(\theta_1 - \delta) + (\theta_2 - \delta)]'A(\theta_1 - \theta_2)$

Obviously, simultaneously adding and subtracting $\delta$ does not alter the value of this expression. Thus one can write (3.9) in the form

$$[(\theta_1 - \delta) + (\theta_2 - \delta)]'A[\theta_1 - \delta) - (\theta_2 - \delta)] =$$
(3.10) $(\theta_1 - \delta)'A(\theta_1 - \delta) - (\theta_2 - \delta)'A(\theta_2 - \delta) =$
$$\| \theta_1 - \delta \|^2 - \| \theta_2 - \delta \|^2$$

and the last part of this step is nothing more than the notation introduced in (2.5). It is easily observed from (3.10) and (3.8) that if (3.2) obtains, then

(3.11) $2(x - \delta)'A(\theta_1 - \theta_2) > \| \theta_1 - \delta \|^2 - \| \theta_2 - \delta \|^2$

also holds. In other words, the $i^{th}$ individual votes for the $1^{st}$ candidate if (3.11) is true.

For the moment, consider x to be a vector selected at random from $f(x)$. Then it is useful to know the mean and variance of one half the quantity on the left hand side of (3.11).

$$E[(x - \delta)'A(\theta_1 - \theta_2)] = 0$$
(3.12)
$$\text{Var}[(x - \delta)'A(\theta_1 - \theta_2)] = (\theta_1 - \theta_2)'A\Sigma A(\theta_1 - \theta_2)$$

The following definition (see (2.6)) is simply a matter of notation.

(3.13) $\sqrt{(\theta_1 - \theta_2)'A\Sigma A(\theta_1 - \theta_2)} = \| \theta_1 - \theta_2 \|^*$

In other words, $\| \theta_1 - \theta_2 \|^*$ is simply the standard deviation of $(x - \delta)'A(\theta_1 - \theta_2)$ when x is considered to be a vector selected at random from $f(x)$.

Consider the following definitions.

(3.14)
$$y = \frac{(x - \delta)'A(\theta_1 - \theta_2)}{\| \theta_1 - \theta_2 \|^*}$$
$$t = \frac{\| \theta_1 - \delta \|^2 - \| \theta_2 - \delta \|^2}{2 \| \theta_1 - \theta_2 \|^*}$$

Then the statement

(3.15) $y > t$

is equivalent to statement (3.11). In other words, those individuals for whom (3.15) is true will vote for the 1st candidate.

Expression (3.15) is useful for analysis. It is desired to investigate the possibility of the 1st candidate being able to select his platform (policies) $\theta_1$ in such a manner that he is certain to win the election if $\theta_1 \neq \theta_2$. (Note that if $\theta_1 = \theta_2$, then neither (3.2) nor (3.3) obtain and the election is equivalent to tossing a coin.) Consider selecting a voter at random from the population $f(x)$. If

$$(3.16) \quad P[(x - \theta_1)'A(x - \theta_1) < (x - \theta_2)'A(x - \theta_2)] > \tfrac{1}{2}$$

so that more than one half of the voters in the population obtain a smaller utility loss from the 1st candidate's platform than from the one of his opponent, then the 1st candidate is certain to win the election. The previous analysis shows that

$$(3.17) \quad P(y > t) > \tfrac{1}{2}$$

is equivalent to (3.16). Furthermore, if $f(x)$ is continuous so that for $\theta_1 \neq \theta_2$

$$(3.18) \quad P[(x - \theta_1)'A(x - \theta_1) = (x - \theta_2)'A(x - \theta_2)] = 0$$

then the 1st candidate wins if and only if (3.17) obtains.

It is now necessary to inquire into the conditions under which (3.17) is true. Suppose that $f(x)$ is a multivariate normal density with mean vector $\delta$ and variance-covariance matrix $\Sigma$. Then it is clear from (3.12) and the definition (3.14) of y that y has a standard normal distribution. Thus (3.17) is true if and only if $t < 0$.

Examine the definition (3.14) of t. Suppose that the 1st candidate selects $\theta_1 = \delta$. Obviously, $\| \delta - \delta \| = 0$. Then for any choice of the 2nd candidate such that $\theta_2 \neq \delta$, $\| \theta_2 - \delta \| > 0$. It follows that $t < 0$ so that (3.17) is true. In other words, if the 1st candidate selects the policies in his platform to be exactly the same as the mean of the policies desired by the individuals in the voting population, and the other candidate does not make the same choice, then the 1st candidate is certain to win the election. Conversely, suppose that the 1st candidate selects $\theta_1 \neq \delta$. Obviously, $\| \theta_1 - \delta \| > 0$ in such an instance. If the 2nd candidate selects $\theta_2 = \delta$, then $\| \theta_2 - \delta \| = 0$ so that $t > 0$. Thus

$$(3.19) \quad P(y > t) < \tfrac{1}{2}$$

is true so that the 2nd candidate is certain to win the election. Finally, if both $\theta_1 = \delta$ and $\theta_2 = \delta$, then it is obvious that a tie is expected. The following theorem is established:

Theorem: 3.1: Given the assumptions resulting in voting rules (3.2) and

(3.3), then, if the density of preferred points $f(x)$ is normal, the platform $\theta = \delta$ is a dominant strategy.

The fact that $\theta = \delta$ insures a candidate of winning the election if the opposing candidate does not make the identical choice of selecting his platform to be the vector of means of the preferred positions, and gives the expectation of a tie if both candidates choose the vector of means, indicates that there should be a tendency for wise candidates to select such policies for their platforms. It is interesting to note that insofar as this tendency is observed, then the competition between candidates in a democratic process tends to produce the policies which a beneficent dictator operating under (3.1) would select.

The above result depends upon the assumed normality of $f(x)$. Since the actual population of voters in any given country is necessarily finite, this assumption means that the presumed normal $f(x)$ is an approximation to the actual density. Now for many cases this approximation will be sufficiently good. Further, one can argue that even if $f(x)$ is not assumed to be a normal density, y can still be approximated by a standard normal in many instances. Yet, one may wonder whether it is possible to say anything when the distribution of preferred points $f(x)$ is not known and no approximations are allowed. The answer is affirmative, at least in the sense that certain bounds can be derived. These bounds are stated in terms of relative deviations from the vector $\delta$ of the means of preferred points, and they indicate the powerful influences of the means upon the policies produced by the democratic process.

Let y and t be defined by (3.14). By beginning with (3.3) and performing steps (3.5 — 3.14), it is seen easily that

(3.20) $y < t$

is equivalent to (3.3). Therefore, those voters for whom (3.20) obtains cast their ballots for the 2nd candidate. Without a loss of generality, consider the case in which

(3.21) $\| \theta_1 - \delta \| > \| \theta_2 - \delta \|$

so that $t > 0$. In other words, the 1st candidate's platform is a greater "distance" from the mean vector of preferred points than is the platform of the 2nd candidate. Noting that $E(y) = 0$ and $Var(y) = 1$, it follows from Tchebyshev's inequality that

(3.22) $P(y < t) \geqslant 1 - 1/t^2$

since the one-sided version of this inequality cannot have a smaller probability of being true than the two-sided one.[10] Further, from the definition (3.14) of t, it is obvious that

$$(3.23)\; \frac{1}{t^2} = \frac{4 \, || \, \theta_1 - \theta_2 \, ||^{*2}}{(|| \, \theta_1 - \delta \, ||^2 - || \, \theta_2 - \delta \, ||^2)^2}$$

For the purpose of the argument, $|| \, \theta_1 - \theta_2 \, ||^*$ must be replaced by a more convenient quantity. Recall that utility is defined uniquely only up to a monotonic transformation. Thus it can be assumed, without loss of generality, that $\not{Z} < A^{-1}$. If this were not so, then A could be multiplied by a positive scalar to make it so without altering any of the analysis or changing anything. It follows that the presumption $A\not{Z}A < A$ is legitimate for the purpose of analysis. Thus

$$(3.24)\; || \, \theta_1 - \theta_2 \, ||^* \leqslant || \, \theta_1 - \theta_2 \, ||$$

follows from this assumption, the definition (3.13) of $|| \, \theta_1 - \theta_2 \, ||^*$ and the definition (2.5) of the norm $|| \cdot ||$ . Also,

$$(3.25)\; || \, \theta_1 - \theta_2 || \leqslant || \, \theta_1 - \delta \, || + || \, \theta_2 - \delta \, ||$$

by the triangle inequality.[11] Noting that

$$(3.26)\; ( \, || \, \theta_1 - \delta \, ||^2 - || \, \theta_2 - \delta \, ||^2 )^2 = ( \, || \, \theta_1 - \delta \, || + || \, \theta_2 - \delta \, || \, )^2 ( \, || \, \theta_1 - \delta \, || - || \, \theta_2 - \delta \, || )^2$$

one can use (3.24) and (3.25) to write

$$(3.27)\; \frac{1}{t^2} \leqslant \frac{4(|| \, \theta_1 - \delta \, || + || \, \theta_2 - \delta \, ||)^2}{(|| \, \theta_1 - \delta \, || + || \, \theta_2 - \delta \, ||)^2 (|| \, \theta_1 - \delta \, || - || \theta_2 - \delta \, ||)^2}$$

Cancelling the common term in the numerator and denominator, one can use (3.27) to write (3.22) in the form

$$(3.28)\; \mathrm{P}(y < t) \geqslant 1 - \frac{4}{(|| \, \theta_1 - \delta \, || - || \, \theta_2 - \delta \, ||)^2}$$

so that if

$$(3.29)\; || \, \theta_1 - \delta \, || - || \, \theta_2 - \delta \, || > 2\sqrt{2}$$

then

$$(3.30)\; \mathrm{P}(y < t) > 1/2$$

so that the 2nd candidate receives more than one-half of the votes.

---

[10] Tchebyshev's inequality can be stated as follows: Let z be a random variable with mean $\delta$ and standard deviation $\sigma$. Then

$$\mathrm{P}( \, | \, z - \delta \, | \leqslant k) \geqslant 1 - \sigma^2/k^2$$

where k is an arbitrary positive number. See, e.g., S. Ehrenfeld and S. Littauer, *Introduction to Statistical Method*, New York: McGraw-Hill, 1964, pp. 132-133, for a proof of an alternative form of Tchebyshev's inequality.

[11] An intuitive understanding of the meaning of the triangle inequality can be gained with recourse to the following example: Let u, r, and s denote three points in space. (One may think of the points u, r, and s as being the three vertices of a triangle.) Then the distance between any two of the points, say u and r, must be less than or equal to the distance between u and s plus the distance between s and r. For a proof of the triangle inequality, see P. R. Halmos, *Finite Dimensional Vector Spaces* (2d ed., Princeton: D. Van Nostrand Co., 1958), pp. 125-26.

It is obvious that if the inequality (3.21) is reversed, an argument similar to the above one can be presented to show that if

(3.31) $\| \theta_2 - \delta \| - \| \theta_1 - \delta \| > 2 \sqrt{2}$

then the $1^{st}$ candidate wins the election. The following theorem is established:

> Theorem: 3.2: Given the assumptions resulting in voting rules (3.2) and (3.3), and given that the elements of $\delta$ and $\sharp$ are finite, then no matter what form the density $f(x)$, (3.29) gives a bound for the 2nd candidate to win and (3.31) gives a bound for the 1st candidate to win.

The vector $\delta$ of the means of the policies preferred by the voters is a powerful influence upon the policies emerging from the competition of the democratic process. If either candidate selects policies which depart radically from these means, then the other candidate can win easily by choosing policies close to these means. Furthermore, it should be pointed out that the Tchebyshev inequality gives a rather generous bound for most distributions. This generosity is increased ever further here not only by the fact that (3.22) is one-sided, but also by the fact that steps (3.24) and (3.25) are inequalities. Hence, it appears that the actual bounds are likely to be narrower than the ones indicated by (3.29) and (3.31). Once again, it appears that the competition of the democratic process tends to force (or at least encourage) the policies which emerge from that process to be not too different from the policies which a beneficent dictator might choose.

In fact, the influence of the vector $\delta$ of means is even more powerful than might be imagined from the previous analysis. Suppose that either of the following is true: (1) The population becomes more sophisticated in the sense that the number of indices required to characterize a given set of issues of policy increases. (2) The number of policy issues increases, thus causing an increase in the number of indices. Let the candidates choose the platforms

(3.32) $\theta_1 = \delta$ ; $\theta_2 = \delta + \epsilon 1, \epsilon \neq 0$

where $\epsilon$ is any non-zero scalar (no matter how small) and

(3.33) $1 = [1, 1, ..., 1]'$

an n component column vector of 1's. Then as the number of independent indices n increases, the proportion of the vote going to the $1^{st}$ candidate increases to one. The only qualification on this proposition is that n must increase in such a manner that the $n \times n$ matrix A remains positive definite. This qualification may be interpreted as meaning that no two indices measure the same policy characteristic.

From (3.15) and (3.14) it can be seen that

$$(3.34) \quad y > -\frac{||\,\theta_2 - \delta\,||^2}{2\,||\,\theta_1 - \theta_2\,||^*} = t$$

is equivalent to (3.2) due to the definition (3.32) of $\theta_1$ and the fact that $||\,\delta - \delta\,|| = 0$. Assuming as before (and without loss of generality) that $\not\!\! A \leqslant A^{-1}$ so that $A\not\!\! A \leqslant A$, then it follows from the definitions (2.4) and (2.6) of the two norms that

$$(3.35) \quad ||\,\theta_1 - \theta_2\,||^* \leqslant ||\,\theta_1 - \theta_2\,|| = ||\,\theta_2 - \delta\,||$$

due to the definition (3.32) of $\theta_1$. Therefore

$$(3.36) \quad \frac{||\,\theta_2 - \delta\,||^2}{2\,||\,\theta_1 - \theta_2\,||^*} \geqslant \frac{||\,\theta_2 - \delta\,||}{2} = (1/2)\,\sqrt{(\theta_2 - \delta)'A(\theta_2 - \delta)}$$

and, noting the definition (3.32) of $\theta_2$, the right hand side of (3.36) is equal to

$$(3.37) \quad (\tfrac{1}{2})\,\sqrt{\epsilon^2\,1'A1} = (|\epsilon|/2)\,\sqrt{1'A1}$$

where 1 is defined by (3.33). Let $e_n$ represent the minimum eigenvalue of the $n \times n$ matrix A.[12] Then $e_n > 0$ due to the fact that the matrix A is assumed to be positive definite.[13] Also, for any positive definite matrix A and any n component vector z

$$(3.38) \quad z'Az \geqslant e_n \sum_{i=1}^{n} z_i^2$$

so that for the case in point

$$(3.39) \quad 1'A1 \geqslant ne_n$$

since the square of one is one and there are n ones in the vector 1. Substituting (3.39) into the right hand side of (3.37), it is easily seen from (3.36) that

$$(3.40) \quad \frac{||\,\theta_2 - \delta\,||^2}{2\,||\,\theta_1 - \theta_2\,||^*} \geqslant \frac{|\epsilon|}{2}\,\sqrt{ne_n}$$

Net $n \rightarrow \infty$ in such a manner that the $n \times n$ matrix A remains positive definite so that the $e_n$ are bounded away from the origin. Then

$$(3.41) \quad \lim_{n \rightarrow \infty} \frac{|\epsilon|}{2}\,\sqrt{ne_n} = \infty$$

and from this limit, definition (3.34) of t, and relationship (3.40), $t \rightarrow -\infty$ as $n \rightarrow \infty$. Therefore

---

[12] An eigenvalue can be defined as follows: Let B represent an $n \times n$ matrix and z an n component column vector. Consider the relationship
$$Bz = \lambda z$$
where $\lambda$ is a scalar. An eigenvalue of the matrix B is some value of the scaler $\lambda$ for which this relationship obtains for $z \neq 0$. A matrix of order n has at most n distinguishable eigenvalues. The discussion above is concerned with the smallest of the eigenvalues of the matrix A.

[13] See, e.g., G. Hadley, *Linear Algebra* (Reading: Addison-Wesley, 1961), p. 256.

(3.42) $P(y > t) \to 1$ as $n \to \infty$

where the 1 in (3.42) is the number one. The following theorem is established:

> Theorem: 3.3: Given the assumptions resulting in voting rules (3.2) and (3.3), and given that the platforms of the two candidates are defined by (3.32), then if $n \to \infty$ while the $n \times n$ matrix A remains positive definite, the fraction of the total vote going to the 1st candidate approaches one.

This theorem indicates the power of the influence of the vector $\delta$ of means of the preferred positions. It also has a number of interesting interpretations. One might infer, for example, that as the population becomes more sophisticated in the manner in which policies are viewed, and as the number of issues of policy increases, then the chance of an extremist candidate winning the election goes down no matter what the density of preferred points.

## 4. *Candidate Selection by Primaries and a General Election*

The analysis of Section 3 ignored the phenomenon of political parties. Certainly, the mere fact that parties select the candidates who run in the general election may place restrictions upon the strategy or platform which the candidates can choose. Even when the terms strategy and platform (used interchangeably here) are defined to mean "that for which the candidate stands" (rather than the formal documents drawn up by the U.S. parties), it must be admitted that in a sense the candidate "represents" the party. Consequently, it is of interest to examine a situation in which a candidate has first to win the nomination in his own party and then must compete in the election on the basis of the same strategy (platform) which won for him the party's nomination.

Let the totality of registered voters be divided into two mutually exclusive and exhaustive populations (parties) which are denoted "one" and "two" respectively.[14] Let $w_i$ represent the preferred position of the $i^{th}$ voter from the $1^{st}$ population and $v_j$ the preferred position of the $j^{th}$ voter from the $2^{nd}$ population. Also, represented by $f_1(w)$ and $f_2(v)$ the respective densities of the preferred positions of the voters of the $1^{st}$ and $2^{nd}$ populations. The means of these densities are defined by

(4.1) $E(w) = \delta_1$ ; $E(v) = \delta_2$

and the variance-covariance matrices are defined by

---

[14] Note that this exhaustive division means that no independent voters are allowed.

$$(4.2) \quad \begin{aligned} E(w - \delta_1)(w - \delta_1)' &= \Sigma_1 \\ E(v - \delta_2)(v - \delta_2)' &= \Sigma_2 \end{aligned}$$

where each $\Sigma$ is $n \times n$. If $\theta$ represents a policy vector, then let

$$(4.3) \quad \begin{aligned} L_{1i}(\theta) &= (w_i - \theta)'A(w_i - \theta) \\ L_{2j}(\theta) &= (v_j - \theta)'A(v_j - \theta) \end{aligned}$$

represent the respective loss functions of the $i^{th}$ and $j^{th}$ voters from the $1^{st}$ and $2^{nd}$ populations. Note especially that the $n \times n$ positive definite matrix A is commmon to all voters in both populations. Of course, it is important to observe that this does not prevent wide differences in taste from existing between the two homogeneous populations since no restrictions are placed upon the preferred positions (the $w_i$ and $v_j$) of the voters in the populations. Differences between the two populations will be discussed in terms of the parameters defined by (4.1) and (4.2). Finally, it is assumed here, as in the previous section, that

$$(4.4) \quad \Sigma_1 \leq A^{-1} \; ; \; \Sigma_2 \leq A^{-1}$$

which, as was explained earlier, is no restriction due to the fact that loss functions are uniquely defined only up to a monotonic transformation.

The analysis here is developed under the assumption that a purely democratic process produces the nominations. This presumption represents something of a departure from reality, at least for the U.S. where conventions have the responsibility for candidate selection.[15] Yet, it is informative to assume that the candidate really does "represent" the party in the sense that he is the winner of an all inclusive within-party election.

By boldly making this assumption and also by presuming that within any party the number of candidates is always two, the analysis of Section 3 can be applied to the nominations. Thus it is assumed that the candidates have platforms which are the means of the preferred points of the members of their respective parties. Accordingly, let $1^{st}$ and $2^{nd}$ candidates be the respective nominees of the $1^{st}$ and $2^{nd}$ parties. Then

$$(4.5) \quad \theta_1 = \delta_1 \; ; \; \theta_2 = \delta_2$$

are presumed to be the respective platforms of the two candidates.

There remains the problem of specifying the voters' rule of

---

[15] The possibility of "bias" is easily seen by adopting Buchanan and Tullock's argument concerning representation to the process of nomination by convention. J. M. Buchanan and G. Tullock, *The Calculus of Consent* (Ann Arbor: University of Michigan Press, 1962), pp. 217-22.

choice between these two candidates in the general election. Ignoring party loyalty, it is presumed that the $i^{th}$ and $j^{th}$ individuals vote for the $1^{st}$ candidate if

$$(4.6) \quad \begin{array}{l} (w_i - \theta_1)'A(w_i - \theta_1) < (w_i - \theta_2)'A(w_i - \theta_2) \\ (v_j - \theta_1)'A(v_j - \theta_1) < (v_j - \theta_2)'A(v_j - \theta_2) \end{array}$$

holds and for the $2^{nd}$ candidate if

$$(4.7) \quad \begin{array}{l} (w_i - \theta_1)'A(w_i - \theta_1) > (w_i - \theta_2)'A(w_i - \theta_2) \\ (v_j - \theta_1)'A(v_j - \theta_1) > (v_j - \theta_2)'A(v_j - \theta_2) \end{array}$$

obtains.[16] Recalling (4.5), it is clear that the voter's choice depends upon the two vectors of means $\delta_1$ and $\delta_2$. Since $\delta_1 \neq \delta_2$ is assumed always, and since $f_1(w)$ and $f_2(v)$ are viewed as being continuous densities, there is no problem in ignoring the possibility of some voter being faced with equal losses from the two platforms.[17]

Once again, it is desirable to get these voting rules into a form more amenable to analysis. By performing the operations exhibited in (3.5-3.10) and recalling that $\theta_1 = \delta_1$ and $\theta_2 = \delta_2$ as stated by (4.5), one obtains

$$(4.8) \quad \begin{array}{l} 2(w - \delta_1)'A(\delta_1 - \delta_2) > -\|\delta_1 - \delta_2\|^2 \\ 2(v - \delta_2)'A(\delta_1 - \delta_2) > \|\delta_1 - \delta_2\|^2 \end{array}$$

as expressions equivalent to those of (4.6). Note that the i and j subscripts are omitted for convenience. It is obvious that

$$(4.9) \quad \begin{array}{l} E[(w - \delta_1)'A(\delta_1 - \delta_2)] = 0 \\ E[(v - \delta_2)'A(\delta_1 - \delta_2)] = 0 \end{array}$$

and it can be shown that

$$(4.10) \quad \begin{array}{l} \mathrm{Var}\,[(w - \delta_1)'A(\delta_1 - \delta_2)] = (\delta_1 - \delta_2)'A\Sigma_1 A(\delta_1 - \delta_2) \\ \mathrm{Var}\,[(v - \delta_2)'A(\delta_1 - \delta_2)] = (\delta_1 - \delta_2)'A\Sigma_2 A(\delta_1 - \delta_2) \end{array}$$

Define as in (2.6)

$$(4.11) \quad \begin{array}{l} \sqrt{(\delta_1 - \delta_2)'A\Sigma_1 A(\delta_1 - \delta_2)} = \|\delta_1 - \delta_2\|_1^* \\ \sqrt{(\delta_1 - \delta_2)'A\Sigma_2 A(\delta_1 - \delta_2)} = \|\delta_1 - \delta_2\|_2^* \end{array}$$

and

$$(4.12) \quad \begin{array}{l} y_1 = \dfrac{(w - \delta_1)'A(\delta_1 - \delta_2)}{\|\delta_1 - \delta_2\|_1^*} \\[2ex] y_2 = \dfrac{(v - \delta_2)'A(\delta_1 - \delta_2)}{\|\delta_1 - \delta_2\|_2^*} \end{array}$$

[16] It might be noted that, at least with some interpretation, the voting rule need not conflict with the notion of party loyalty. See the discussion in Chapters 3 and 5 of A. Campbell, P. E. Converse, W. E. Miller, and D. E. Stokes, *The American Voter* (New York: Wiley, 1960).

[17] Of course, it is easy to take the equal loss possibility into account by assuming that in such an instance a voter will choose the candidate of his own party. The point is that this additional assumption does not alter the results of the analysis.

so that

(4.13) $E(y_1)=0$  ;  $E(y_2)=0$

and

(4.14) $\text{Var}(y_1)=1$  ;  $\text{Var}(y_2)=1$

Also define

$$t_1 = -\frac{||\,\delta_1 - \delta_2\,||^2}{2\,||\,\delta_1 - \delta_2\,||_1^*}$$

(4.15)

$$t_2 = \frac{||\,\delta_1 - \delta_2\,||^2}{2\,||\,\delta_1 - \delta_2\,||_2^*}$$

It follows that

(4.16) $y_1 > t_1$  ;  $y_2 > t_2$

is equivalent to (4.6). In other words, voters from the 1st and 2nd parties respectively cast their ballots for the 1st candidate if and only if (4.16) obtains.

It is necessary to obtain an expression for the portion (fraction) of the total vote which the 1st candidate receives. Let $\alpha$ represent that fraction of the total number of voters belonging to the 1st party. Then $1 - \alpha$ represents the fraction of the total number of voters belonging to the 2nd party. Imagine selecting a voter at random from each of the 1st and 2nd populations. Then

(4.17) $R = \alpha P(y_1 > t_1) + (1 - \alpha)P(y_2 > t_2)$

represents the fraction of the total vote going to the 1st candidate. Obviously, $1 - R$ is the fraction of the vote going to the 2nd candidate. Thus the 1st candidate wins the election if $R > \frac{1}{2}$, and the 2nd candidate wins if $R < \frac{1}{2}$.

Recall that the norm $||\,\delta_1 - \delta_2\,||$ can be interpreted as the "distance" between the mean vectors of the two populations. It is of interest to determine the effect of increases in this distance.

From assumption (4.4) and the definitions (2.4) and (4.11) of the two types of norms under consideration here, it follows that

(4.18) $||\,\delta_1 - \delta_2\,|| \geqslant ||\,\delta_1 - \delta_2\,||_k^*$ ,  $k=1, 2$.

This means that

$$t_1 \leqslant -\frac{||\,\delta_1 - \delta_2\,||}{2}$$

(4.19)

$$t_2 \geqslant \frac{||\,\delta_1 - \delta_2\,||}{2}$$

Let distance between the two mean vectors increase. As $||\,\delta_1 - \delta_2\,|| \to \infty$, then from (4.19) $t_1 \to -\infty$ and $t_2 \to \infty$ so that $P(y_1 > t_1) \to 1$ and $P(y_2 > t_2) \to 0$. From (4.17), $R \to \alpha$. Thus as the distance between the mean vectors of the two parties increases, voters tend to stick more and more with their own parties until in the limit the minority party has no chance and the majority party always wins. One can speculate that such a situation, where there are large differences between the (opposing) desires of the two groups and the minority has no chance of exerting any influence upon policy, is not very conducive to the continuation of a democracy. It is plausible to believe that conflict is likely to result and it is interesting to ponder real world situations such as the Cyprus problem in the light of this result.

It is appropriate to consider the relationship between the manner in which the total vote is divided and the parameters $\mathcal{X}_1$ and $\mathcal{X}_2$. Letting $\| \delta_1 - \delta_2 \|$ be a finite number, suppose that

(4.20) $\mathcal{X}_1 \geq \mathcal{X}_2$

so that the 1st party is allowed to represent a "wider range" of taste or opinion than is the 2nd party. Granted this greater spread of preferred points, it is interesting to determine the conditions under which the 1st party's candidate can win the election.

Let both $f_1(w)$ and $f_2(v)$ be multivariate normal densities. Then it is easily seen from the definition (4.12) that both $y_1$ and $y_2$ are normally distributed with zero means and unit variances. Define

$$(4.21) \quad k_1 = \frac{\| \delta_1 - \delta_2 \|^2}{2 \| \delta_1 - \delta_2 \|_1^*} = -t_1$$

$$k_2 = -\frac{\| \delta_1 - \delta_2 \|^2}{2 \| \delta_1 - \delta_2 \|_2^*} = -t_2$$

so that by the symmetry of the unit normal distribution

$$(4.22) \quad \begin{aligned} P(y_1 > t_1) &= P(y_1 < k_1) \\ P(y_2 > t_2) &= P(y_2 < k_2) \end{aligned}$$

and (4.17) can be written equivalently

(4.23) $R = \alpha P(y_1 < k_1) + (1 - \alpha) P(y_2 < k_2)$

Note that $k_1 > 0$ so that $P(y_1 < k_1) > \frac{1}{2}$ and $k_2 < 0$ so that $P(y_2 < k_2) < \frac{1}{2}$.

If the 1st candidate is to win the election, then it must be the case that his fraction of the vote is greater than one half ($R > \frac{1}{2}$). Making this assumption, one may obtain from (4.23)

$$(4.24) \quad \alpha > \frac{\frac{1}{2} - P(y_2 < k_2)}{P(y_1 < k_1) - P(y_2 < k_2)} > 0$$

Granted the assumption (4.20), it is easily seen from the definition (4.11) of the starred norms that

$$(4.25) \quad \| \delta_1 - \delta_2 \|_1^* \geq \| \delta_1 - \delta_2 \|_2^*$$

From $(4.25)$ and definition $(4.21)$ one observes that $k_1 \leqslant - k_2$ so that

$(4.26)$ $(Py_1 < k_1) \leqslant P(y_2 < - k_2) = 1 - P(y_2 < k_2)$

and by substitution

$(4.27)$ $\dfrac{\frac{1}{2} - P(y_2 < k_2)}{P(y_1 < k_1) - P(y_2 < k_2)} \geqslant \dfrac{\frac{1}{2} - P(y_2 < k_2)}{1 - 2P(y_2 < k_2)} = \frac{1}{2}$

It follows from $(4.27)$ and $(4.24)$ that $\alpha > \frac{1}{2}$. In other words, if the 1st party is more "dispersed" than the 2nd party in the sense that its members have more divergent points of view, opinions, and desires for policies; if both parties choose candidates whose respective platforms represent the party's vector of means of the preferred positions of its members; and if the densities of preferred positions are normal; then the 1st party can win the election only if it is the majority party. Obviously, the converse of this statement is also true. If the 1st party is a minority $(\alpha < \frac{1}{2})$, and if $(4.20)$ obtains, then the 1st candidate loses the election.

The above discussion makes clear the fact that the minority party can win under certain conditions. Therefore, one might be interested in determining when a minority triumph can take place. Note that if $(4.24)$ is true, then it is implied that

$(4.28)$ $\frac{1}{2} < \alpha P(y_1 < k_1) + (1 - \alpha)P(y_2 < k_2)$

so that the candidate of the 1st party must win the election. Therefore, it is important to investigate whether and under what conditions $(4.24)$ can obtain when $\alpha < \frac{1}{2}$.

Let it be assumed that $\alpha < \frac{1}{2}$ and

$(4.29)$ $\not z_1 < \not z_2$

so that the 1st party is more "cohesive" than the 2nd one in the sense that it represents a "smaller range" of taste and opinion about policy. Then the above analysis would tend to indicate that it is possible for the 1st party to win the election. In order to explain easily why this can be true, allow the following somewhat more stringent, assumption to be made.

$(4.30)$ $c^2 \not z_1 = \not z_2, c > 1$

Granted condition $(4.30)$, definitions $(4.11)$ imply

$(4.31)$ $c \, \| \, \delta_1 - \delta_2 \, \|_1^* = \| \, \delta_1 - \delta_2 \, \|_2^*$

and applying $(4.31)$ to definitions $(4.21)$ yields

$(4.32)$ $k_2 = - k_1/c$

so that substitution is possible. Noting that $k_1 > 0$ so that $P(y_1 < k_1) > \frac{1}{2}$, let $c \to \infty$. Then $- k_1/c \to 0$ so that $P(y_2 < - k_1/c) \to \frac{1}{2}$. Applying these results to $(4.24)$ gives

$$(4.33) \quad \alpha > \frac{\frac{1}{2} - P(y_2 < -k_1/c)}{P(y_1 < k_1) - P(y_2 < -k_1/c)} \to 0$$

so that $\alpha < \frac{1}{2}$ is certainly possible when (4.24) obtains. Since (4.24) implies (4.28), the candidate of the 1st party wins the election.

An intuitive understanding of the above result can be obtained by recourse to a simple graph. Assume a single index of a single issue so that $n = 1$. In Figure 3 the densities $f_1(w)$ and $f_2(v)$ are plotted and the means (the respective candidates' platforms) are appropriately indicated. Note that the variance of the density of preferred points for the 1st party is much smaller than the variance of the 2nd party. Inspection of the diagram makes clear the fact that the 1st party's candidate will obtain the votes of almost all the members of his own party and will also receive the votes of some members of the 2nd party. Thus the candidate of the 1st party can win even though his party is a minority.

It is interesting to speculate about the rise of the Nazi party in Germany in the light of this result. It is also interesting to consider Communist Party participation in the elections in certain countries in terms of this result.

## 5. Platforms and the General Election

The analysis of the above section suggests an interesting question. Suppose that one or both of the parties is something less than purely democratic in the selection of its candidate. Can the party improve its chances in the general election by carefully selecting a candidate whose personal platform is something of a "compromise" between the desires of the members of the candidate's own party and those of the members of the other party? The answer seems to be affirmative. Granted the existence of two populations (parties), this section is devoted to the demonstration of two propositions, both of which depend upon normality. First, it will be shown that there exists some convex combination of the two vectors of means which is at least as good as any other type of strategy. Second, it will be shown that there exists a particular convex combination which dominates all others.

Let $f_1(w)$ and $f_2(v)$ be multivariate normal densities whose means are given by (4.1) and variance-covariance matrices by (4.2). Let (4.6) and (4.7) define the voting rule. Then for any platforms $\theta_1$ and $\theta_2$ such that $\theta_1 \neq \theta_2$, it can be shown by repeating steps (3.5-3.15) that voters from the respective populations choose the 1st candidate if

$$(5.1)$$
$$y_1 = \frac{(w - \delta_1)'A(\theta_1 - \theta_2)}{|| \theta_1 - \theta_2 ||_1^*} > \frac{|| \theta_1 - \delta_1 ||^2 - || \theta_2 - \delta_1 ||^2}{2 || \theta_1 - \theta_2 ||_1^*} = t_1$$

$$y_2 = \frac{(v - \delta_2)'A(\theta_1 - \theta_2)}{|| \theta_1 - \theta_2 ||_2^*} > \frac{|| \theta_1 - \delta_2 ||^2 - || \theta_2 - \delta_2 ||^2}{2 || \theta_1 - \theta_2 ||_2^*} = t_2$$

where the subscriptions on v and w are omitted for convenience. Obviously, if one thinks of selecting a voter at random from each of the two populations, $y_1$ and $y_2$ are distributed as standard normal variables. Thus a sufficient condition for the 1st candidate to win the election in the respective populations is

$$(5.2)$$
$$P(y_1 > t_1) > \tfrac{1}{2}$$
$$P(y_2 > t_2) > \tfrac{1}{2}$$

and this requires $t_1 < 0$ and $t_2 < 0$. From (5.1) it is clear that (5.2) obtains only if

$$(5.3)$$
$$|| \theta_1 - \delta_1 || < || \theta_2 - \delta_1 ||$$
$$|| \theta_1 - \delta_2 || < || \theta_2 - \delta_2 ||$$

so that determining that(5.3) obtains is equivalent to finding that the 1st candidate will win the election.

Consider the first proposition. Let the 1st candidate choose a convex combination of the two vectors of means. Thus

$$(5.4) \quad \theta_1 = \beta_1 \delta_1 + (1 - \beta_1)\delta_2 \quad , \quad 0 \leqslant \beta_1 \leqslant 1$$

represents a strategy which is to be shown to win or tie any non-convex combination $\theta_2$ chosen by the 2nd candidate. Note specifically that since $\theta_2$ is not a convex combination of $\delta_1$ and $\delta_2$, the strategies $\theta_2 = \delta_1$ and $\theta_2 = \delta_2$ are ruled out.

Suppose that the 2nd candidate chooses a platform $\theta_2$ such that

$$(5.5) \quad || \theta_2 - \delta_1 || > || \delta_1 - \delta_2 ||$$

so that the "distance" from $\theta_2$ to the mean $\delta_1$ of the 1st population is greater than distance between the two means. Let the 1st candidate choose $\beta_1 = 0$ so that $\theta_1 = \delta_2$. Then

$$(5.6) \quad || \theta_1 - \delta_1 || = || \delta_1 - \delta_2 || < || \theta_2 - \delta_1 ||$$

so that the 1st candidate wins in the 1st population. Similarly,

$$(5.7) \quad || \theta_1 - \delta_2 || = || \delta_2 - \delta_2 || = 0 < || \theta_2 - \delta_2 ||$$

so that the 1st candidate also wins in the 2nd population.

Alternatively, suppose that the 2nd candidate chooses a platform $\theta_2$ such that

$$(5.8) \quad || \theta_2 - \delta_2 || > || \delta_1 - \delta_2 ||$$

Then let the 1st candidate select $\beta_1 = 1$ so that $\theta_1 = \delta_1$. Thus
$$(5.9) \quad || \theta_1 - \delta_1 || = || \delta_1 - \delta_1 || = 0 < || \theta_2 - \delta_1 ||$$
so that the 1st candidate wins in the 1st population and
$$(5.10) \quad || \theta_1 - \delta_2 || = || \delta_1 - \delta_2 || < || \theta_2 - \delta_2 ||$$
so that the 1st candidate also wins in the 2nd population.

The above results mean that one only need to consider the case in which $\theta_2$ is such that both
$$(5.11) \quad \begin{aligned} || \theta_2 - \delta_1 || < || \delta_1 - \delta_2 || \\ || \theta_2 - \delta_2 || < || \delta_1 - \delta_2 || \end{aligned}$$
obtain. Accordingly, presume that the 2nd candidate chooses a $\theta_2$ such that it is not a convex combination of $\delta_1$ and $\delta_2$ but does satisfy (5.11). By manipulating (5.4) and taking norms of the results one can obtain
$$(5.12) \quad \begin{aligned} || \theta_1 - \delta_1 || = (1 - \beta_1) || \delta_1 - \delta_2 || \\ || \theta_1 - \delta_2 || = \beta_1 || \delta_1 - \delta_2 || \end{aligned}$$
Suppose that the 1st candidate chooses
$$(5.13) \quad \beta_1 = \frac{|| \theta_2 - \delta_2 ||}{|| \delta_1 - \delta_2 ||}$$
and note that $0 \leqslant \beta_1 < 1$ by (5.11). Substituting (5.13) into the 2nd of the equalities (5.12),
$$(5.14) \quad || \theta_1 - \delta_2 || = || \theta_2 - \delta_2 ||$$
so that the 1st and 2nd candidates tie in the 2nd population. Substituting (5.13) into the 1st of the equalities (5.12),
$$(5.15) \quad || \theta_1 - \delta_1 || = || \delta_1 - \delta_2 || - || \theta_2 - \delta_2 ||$$
and noting by the triangle inequality that
$$(5.16) \quad || \delta_1 - \delta_2 || \leqslant || \theta_2 - \delta_1 || + || \theta_2 - \delta_2 ||$$
so that by substituting (5.16) into (5.15)
$$(5.17) \quad || \theta_1 - \delta_1 || \leqslant || \theta_2 - \delta_1 ||$$
and the 1st candidate at worst ties in the 1st population. In fact, it can be shown that for any $\beta_1$ such that
$$(5.18) \quad \frac{|| \delta_1 - \delta_2 || - || \theta_2 - \delta_1 ||}{|| \delta_1 - \delta_2 ||} \leqslant \beta_1 \leqslant \frac{|| \theta_2 - \delta_2 ||}{|| \delta_1 - \delta_2 ||}$$
where $\theta_1$ is given by (5.4), the 1st candidate wins or at worst ties in the general election. Note that, by the triangle inequality, there is at least one $\beta_1$ in the interval. The following theorem is established:

Theorem: 5.1: Given the assumptions resulting in the voting rule (4.6) and (4.7), given that the densities of the preferred positions of the members of the two populations are normal, and given that one candidate selects a platform which is not a convex combination of the two vectors of means; then there exists a platform which is a convex combination of the two vectors of means such that the candidate choosing the latter platform will either win or tie in the general election.

The above theorem means that the strategy of selecting as a platform a convex combination of the two vectors of means can be at least as good as any other type of platform which can be devised. Therefore, it can be argued that if both candidates are free to choose whatever platform they desire, each should select a convex combination of the two vectors of means.

Suppose not only that $\theta_1$ is given by (5.4) but also that the 2nd candidate selects a platform

(5.19) $\quad \theta_2 = \beta_2 \delta_1 + (1 - \beta_2) \delta_2 \quad , \quad 0 \leqslant \beta_2 \leqslant 1$

so that attention is now centered on the instance in which both candidates have these convex combinations as their platforms. It is to be shown that there exists a particular convex combination which wins over all other convex combinations.

In a manner similar to that in which (5.12) was obtained, one may manipulate (5.19) and express the results in terms of norms to get

$$(5.20) \quad \begin{aligned} \| \theta_2 - \delta_1 \| &= (1 - \beta_2) \, \| \delta_1 - \delta_2 \| \\ \| \theta_2 - \delta_2 \| &= \beta_2 \, \| \delta_1 - \delta_2 \| \end{aligned}$$

By substituting (5.20) and (5.12) into the conditions (5.3) for the 1st candidate to win in the respective populations, it is clear that $\beta_1 > \beta_2$ is required in the 1st population and $\beta_1 < \beta_2$ is required in the 2nd population. Therefore, if the two candidates choose the respective platforms (5.4) and (5.19), the fact that the 1st candidate wins in one population implies that the 2nd candidate wins in the other population.

Recall that the fraction of the total vote going to the 1st candidate is

(5.21) $\quad R = \alpha P(y_1 > t_1) + (1 - \alpha) P(y_2 > t_2)$

By noting that $y_1$ and $y_2$ are both distributed as unit normal variates, it follows that

$$(5.22) \quad \begin{aligned} P(y_1 > t_1) &= P(y_1 < -t_1) \\ P(y_2 > t_2) &= P(y_2 < -t_2) \end{aligned}$$

so that

(5.23) $\quad R = \alpha P(y_1 < -t_1) + (1 - \alpha) P(y_2 < -t_2)$

is equivalent to (5.21).

It is desirable to get the expressions for $t_1$ and $t_2$ into forms more suitable for analysis. By the definitions (5.4) of $\theta_1$ and (5.19) of $\theta_2$, it is easily seen that

$$(5.24) \quad \theta_1 - \theta_2 = (\beta_1 - \beta_2)\delta_1 + (\beta_2 - \beta_1)\delta_2 = (\beta_1 - \beta_2)(\delta_1 - \delta_2)$$

so that by taking the appropriate norm

$$(5.25) \quad \| \theta_1 - \theta_2 \|_r^* = |\beta_1 - \beta_2| \, \| \delta_1 - \delta_2 \|_r^* \quad , \quad r = 1, 2$$

where

$$(5.26) \quad \| \delta_1 - \delta_2 \|_r^* = \sqrt{(\delta_1 - \delta_2)' A_r' A_r (\delta_1 - \delta_2)} \quad , \quad r = 1, 2.$$

By recalling the definition (5.1) of $t_1$, substituting from the 1st of the equivalences of (5.12) and (5.20) for the appropriate terms in the numerator, and substituting (5.25) for the denominator,

$$(5.27) \quad -t_1 = \frac{[(1 - \beta_2)^2 - (1 - \beta_1)^2] \, \| \delta_1 - \delta_2 \|^2}{2 |\beta_1 - \beta_2| \, \| \delta_1 - \delta_2 \|_1^*}$$

$$-t_1 = \frac{(2 - \beta_1 - \beta_2)(\beta_1 - \beta_2) \, \| \delta_1 - \delta_2 \|^2}{2 |\beta_1 - \beta_2| \, \| \delta_1 - \delta_2 \|_1^*}$$

are obtained easily after appropriate manipulation.

It is now necessary to make an assumption concerning the relative magnitudes of $\beta_1$ and $\beta_2$. There are two cases to be considered. First, presume that $\beta_1 > \beta_2$ so that $(\beta_1 - \beta_2) = |\beta_1 - \beta_2|$. Thus it follows from the last expression of (5.27) that

$$(5.28) \quad -t_1 = (1 - \lambda)s_1 \quad , \quad \beta_1 > \beta_2$$

where

$$(5.29) \quad \begin{aligned} \lambda &= \frac{(\beta_1 + \beta_2)}{2} \\ s_1 &= \frac{\| \delta_1 - \delta_2 \|^2}{\| \delta_1 - \delta_2 \|_1^*} \end{aligned}$$

By repeating these steps with respect to $t_2$, it is easily seen that

$$(5.30) \quad -t_2 = -\lambda s_2 \quad , \quad \beta_1 > \beta_2$$

where

$$(5.31) \quad s_2 = \frac{\| \delta_1 - \delta_2 \|^2}{\| \delta_1 - \delta_2 \|_2^*}$$

and note that both $s_1$ and $s_2$ are positive constants while $\lambda$ is a variable. Expressions (5.28) and (5.30) are useful for analysis.

It is now necessary to consider the instance in which $\beta_1 < \beta_2$ so that $(\beta_1 - \beta_2) = -|\beta_1 - \beta_2|$. By noting the last of the expressions in (5.27), it is easily seen that

$$(5.32) \quad -t_1 = -(1 - \lambda)s_1 \quad , \quad \beta_1 < \beta_2$$

and it also follows that

$$(5.33) \quad -t_2 = \lambda s_2 \quad , \quad \beta_1 < \beta_2$$

and expressions (5.32) and (5.33) are useful for analysis.

Define $R_1(\lambda)$ to be the fraction of the total vote going to the 1$^{st}$ candidate when $\beta_1 > \beta_2$. Then from (5.30), (5.28), and (5.23)

(5.34)  $R_1(\lambda) = \alpha P[y_1 < (1-\lambda)s_1] + (1-\alpha)P[y_2 < -\lambda s_2]$

and recalling that $y_1$ and $y_2$ are unit normal variates

$$(5.35) \quad \frac{dR_1(\lambda)}{d\lambda} = -\alpha \frac{s_1}{\sqrt{2\pi}} \exp\left[-\frac{(1-\lambda)^2 s_1^2}{2}\right]$$

$$-(1-\alpha)\frac{s_2}{\sqrt{2\pi}} \exp\left[-\frac{\lambda^2 s_2^2}{2}\right] < 0$$

so it follows that $R_1(\lambda)$ is a monotonically decreasing function of $\lambda$ in the interval $0 \leqslant \lambda \leqslant 1$.

Define $R_2(\lambda)$ to be the fraction of the total vote going to the 1$^{st}$ candidate when $\beta_1 < \beta_2$. Then from (5.33), (5.32) and (5.23)

(5.36)  $R_2(\lambda) = \alpha P[y_1 < -(1-\lambda)s_1] + (1-\alpha)P[y_2 < \lambda s_2]$

but by noting that

$$(5.37) \quad \begin{aligned} P[y_1 < -(1-\lambda)s_1] &= 1 - P[y_1 < (1-\lambda)s_1] \\ P[y_2 < \lambda s_2] &= 1 - P[y_2 < -\lambda s_2] \end{aligned}$$

(5.36) can be written

(5.38)  $R_2(\lambda) = 1 - R_1(\lambda)$

so that $R_2(\lambda)$ is a monotonically increasing function of $\lambda$ in the interval $0 \leqslant \lambda \leqslant 1$.

From the monotonic properties of $R_1(\lambda)$ and $R_2(\lambda)$, and from expression (5.38), it follows that there must exist a value $\lambda^*$ of $\lambda$ such that

(5.39)  $R_1(\lambda^*) = R_2(\lambda^*) = \frac{1}{2}$

Now suppose that the 1$^{st}$ candidate chooses $\beta_1 = \lambda^*$. Then there are two cases to be examined.

Suppose first that $\lambda^* = \beta_1 > \beta_2$. Thus

(5.40)  $\lambda = (\beta_1 + \beta_2)2 < \beta_1 = \lambda^*$

and as $\beta_1 > \beta_2$, $R_1(\lambda)$ must be examined. Since from (5.40) $\lambda < \lambda^*$, and due to the fact that $R_1(\lambda)$ is a monotonically decreasing function of $\lambda$,

(5.41)  $R_1(\lambda) > R_1(\lambda^*) = \frac{1}{2}$

so that the 1$^{st}$ candidate wins the election.

Suppose next that $\lambda^* = \beta_1 < \beta_2$. Then

(5.42)  $\lambda = (\beta_1 + \beta_2)/2 > \beta_1 = \lambda^*$

and as $\beta_1 < \beta_2$, $R_2(\lambda)$ must be examined. Since $\lambda > \lambda^*$ from (5.42), and due to the fact that $R_2(\lambda)$ is a monotonically increasing function of $\lambda$.

(5.43)  $R_2(\lambda) > R_2(\lambda^*) = \frac{1}{2}$

so that the 1$^{st}$ candidate wins the election.

Relations (5.41) and (5.43) show that the particular convex combination

(5.44) $\theta^* = \lambda^* \delta_1 + (1 - \lambda^*) \delta_2$

wins over all other convex combinations. Of course, if both candidates select (5.44), then a tie is expected in the election. The following theorem is established:

> Theorem: 5.2: Given the assumptions resulting in the voting rule (4.6) and (4.7), given that the densities of the preferred positions of the members of the two populations are normal, and given that the two candidates select their platforms from the class (5.4) and (5.19), then the platform (5.44) is a dominant strategy.

The above theorems have an interesting implication for the process by which parties select candidates. From Section 3 it is clear that the vector of means of the preferred positions of the party membership exerts a powerful influence upon the platform of a candidate emerging from a truly representative, democratic process. It can be argued that in the Western World there are powerful forces causing the parties to become "more democratic" in regard to nominations. Yet, both of the above theorems indicate that a party can improve its chances of winning by giving consideration to the preferences of the members of the other party. The "dilemma of nominations" is that if the party membership is not able to take a strategic point of view and if "political bosses" are able to take such a point of view, then having the "smoke-filled cloakroom nominations" may improve the party's chances in the election.

There are two unfortunate points to be made. First, the fact that the above theorems are separate implies that it is unknown whether (5.44) is a dominant strategy overall. Second, the proof of theorem 5.2 is not constructive in the sense that the numerical value of $\lambda^*$ is unknown. Therefore, it may be useful to present a simple example.

Suppose that $\alpha = \frac{1}{2}$. Then it is easy to verify from (5.39) that

(5.45) $P[y_1 < (1 - \lambda^*)s_1] + P[y_2 < -\lambda^* s_2] = 1$

or, by noting the last of the relationships (5.37),

(5.46) $P[y_1 < (1 - \lambda^*)s_1] = P[y_2 < \lambda^* s_2]$

so that by defining

(5.47) $\lambda^* = \dfrac{s_1}{s_1 + s_2}$

relationship (5.46) is satisfied. If in addition $\bar{x}_1 = \bar{x}_2$ so that $s_1 = s_2$, then $\lambda^* = \frac{1}{2}$ and the dominant strategy

(5.48) $\theta^* = (\delta_1 + \delta_2)/2$

is a simple average of the two vectors of means.

## 6. A Simple Extension

All of the previous analysis presumes a certain homogeneity of the taste of voters in the sense that the matrix A enters all loss functions. While this assumption is convenient, it does not allow for the simple situation in which some voters do not care about some subset of issues. Accordingly, one situation of this type is considered here.

Again let the totality of voters be divided into two mutually exclusive and exhaustive populations. Let $w_i$ and $v_j$ be n component vectors representing the preferred positions of the $i^{th}$ voter in the 1st population and the $j^{th}$ voter in the 2nd population respectively. Then $f_1(w)$ and $f_2(v)$ represent the densities of the preferred positions. The mean vectors are given by (4.1) and the variance-covariance matrices by (4.2).

Instead of using the matrix A in all loss functions, let

$$\text{(6.1)} \quad \begin{aligned} L_{1i}(\theta) &= (w_i - \theta)'A_1(w_i - \theta) \\ L_{2j}(\theta) &= (v_j - \theta)'A_2(v_j - \theta) \end{aligned}$$

represent the respective loss functions of the $i^{th}$ and $j^{th}$ voters from the 1st and 2nd populations. Suppose that both $A_1$ and $A_2$ are singular $n \times n$ matrices and are given by

$$\text{(6.2)} \quad A_1 = \begin{bmatrix} M & O \\ O & O \end{bmatrix} \qquad A_2 = \begin{bmatrix} O & O \\ O & N \end{bmatrix}$$

where M is an $m \times m$ positive definite matrix $(m < n)$ and N is a $(n-m) \times (n-m)$ positive definite matrix. Note that the specification of $A_1$ means that all voters in the 1st population obtain possible utility losses only from the first m components of political choice. Therefore, these voters do not care about the last $(n-m)$ components of choice. Similarly, the specification of $A_2$ implies that all voters in the 2nd population obtain possible utility losses only from the last $(n-m)$ components of political choice and do not care about the first m components. Note that $A_1A_2 = 0$. One might say that there is no interaction between the desires of the two populations.

It might be observed that the specification (6.2) of $A_1$ and $A_2$ raises a question concerning the legitimacy of calling $w_i$ and $v_j$ the preferred positions of $i^{th}$ and $j^{th}$ voters. The following developments should make clear the fact that the difficulty is entirely terminological.

Presuming the existence of two candidates with the platforms $\theta_1$ and $\theta_2$ where $\theta_1 \neq \theta_2$, it can be shown by postulating the usual voting rules and repeating steps (3.5-3.15) that voters from the respective populations choose the 1$^{st}$ candidate if

$$
\begin{aligned}
(6.3) \quad & y_1 = \frac{(w - \delta_1)'A_1(\theta_1 - \theta_2)}{\|\theta_1 - \theta_2\|_1^{*}} > \frac{\|\theta_1 - \delta_1\|_1^{2} - \|\theta_2 - \delta_1\|_1^{2}}{2\|\theta_1 - \theta_2\|_1^{*}} = t_1 \\
& y_2 = \frac{(v - \delta_2)'A_2(\theta_1 - \theta_2)}{\|\theta_1 - \theta_2\|_2^{*}} > \frac{\|\theta_1 - \delta_2\|_2^{2} - \|\theta_2 - \delta_2\|_2^{2}}{2\|\theta_1 - \theta_2\|_2^{*}} = t_2
\end{aligned}
$$

and note the subscripts on the norms in the numerators of the terms on the right of the inequalities. These norms must be examined in some detail.

By definition

$$
(6.4) \quad
\begin{aligned}
\|\theta_1 - \delta_1\|_1^{2} &= (\theta_1 - \delta_1)'A_1(\theta_1 - \delta_1) \\
\|\theta_1 - \delta_2\|_2^{2} &= (\theta_1 - \delta_2)'A_2(\theta - \delta_2)
\end{aligned}
$$

but the specifications (6.2) of $A_1$ and $A_2$ indicates that (6.4) can be expressed in a more useful manner. Let $(\theta_1 - \delta_1)_m$ represent a vector composed of the first m components of $(\theta_1 - \delta_1)$. Similarly, let $(\theta_1 - \delta_2)_r$ represent a vector composed of the last $r = n - m$ components of $(\theta_1 - \delta_2)$. Then (6.2) implies

$$
(6.5) \quad
\begin{aligned}
(\theta_1 - \delta_1)'A_1(\theta_1 - \delta_1) &= (\theta_1 - \delta_1)_m'M(\theta_1 - \delta_1)_m \\
(\theta_1 - \delta_2)'A_2(\theta_1 - \delta_2) &= (\theta_1 - \delta_2)_r'N(\theta_1 - \delta_2)_r
\end{aligned}
$$

so that only the first m components of $(\theta_1 - \delta_1)$ are involved in the norm $\|\theta_1 - \delta_1\|_1$ and only the last $r = n - m$ components of $(\theta_1 - \delta_2)$ are involved in the norm $\|\theta_1 - \delta_2\|_2$. By similar definitions and using the same argument

$$
(6.6) \quad
\begin{aligned}
\|\theta_2 - \delta_1\|_1^{2} &= (\theta_2 - \delta_1)_m'M(\theta_2 - \delta_1)_m \\
\|\theta_2 - \delta_2\|_2^{2} &= (\theta_2 - \delta_2)_r'N(\theta_2 - \delta_2)_r
\end{aligned}
$$

so that respectively the first m and last r components are involved in these norms also.

Essentially the same phenomenon is observed in the norms in the denominators of the terms in (6.3). Let $(\theta_1 - \theta_2)_m$ represent a vector composed of the first m components of $(\theta_1 - \theta_2)$. Similarly, let $(\theta_1 - \theta_2)_r$ represent a vector composed of the last $r = n - m$ components of $(\theta_1 - \theta_2)$. Note that

$$
(6.7) \quad A_1 \Sigma_1 A_1 = \begin{bmatrix} M\Sigma_{11}M & 0 \\ 0 & 0 \end{bmatrix} \qquad A_2 \Sigma_2 A_2 = \begin{bmatrix} 0 & 0 \\ 0 & N\Sigma_{22}N \end{bmatrix}
$$

where $\Sigma_{11}$ is the m$\times$m submatrix made up of the first m rows and m columns of $\Sigma_1$ and $\Sigma_{22}$ is the r$\times$r submatrix made up of the last r rows and r columns of $\Sigma_2$. Thus.

$$(6.8) \quad \begin{aligned} \| \theta_1 - \theta_2 \|_1^* &= \sqrt{(\theta_1 - \theta_2)_m' M \Sigma_{11} M (\theta_1 - \theta_2)_m} \\ \| \theta_1 - \theta_2 \|_2^* &= \sqrt{(\theta_1 - \theta_2)_r' N \Sigma_{22} N (\theta_1 - \theta_2)_r} \end{aligned}$$

follows by definition.

By combining (6.4) and (6.5) and substituting the result into (6.3), and by substituting (6.6) and (6.8) into (6.3), it is easy to see the following fact. For all voters in the 1$^{st}$ population the choice of a candidate depends only upon the first m components of the vectors w, $\delta_1$, $\theta_1$, and $\theta_2$. Similarly, for all voters in the 2$^{nd}$ population the choice of a candidate depends only upon the last $r = n - m$ components of the vectors v, $\delta_2$, $\theta_1$, and $\theta_2$. It also follows that the last r components of the vectors w and the first m components of the vectors v can be arbitrarily specified without affecting the analysis.

Suppose that $\theta_1$ is a dominant strategy in the 1$^{st}$ population and $\theta_2$ is a dominant platform in the 2$^{nd}$ population. (If $f_1(w)$ and $f_2(v)$ are multivariate normals, then $\theta_1 = \delta_1$ and $\theta_2 = \delta_2$.) Define a new vector $\overline{\theta}$ which is composed of the first m components of $\theta_1$ and the last $r = n - m$ components of $\theta_2$. Then the voters of the 1$^{st}$ population, for whom only the first m components are relevant, view $\overline{\theta}$ as identically the same as $\theta_1$. Similarly, the voters in the 2$^{nd}$ population, for whom only the last r components are relevant, view $\overline{\theta}$ as identically the same as $\theta_2$. It follows that $\overline{\theta}$ is dominant in both the 1$^{st}$ and 2$^{nd}$ populations and, therefore, wins over any other strategy in the general election. The following theorem is established:

> Theorem: 6.1: Given the assumptions resulting in the voting rules (6.3) and the specification (6.2) of the matrices $A_1$ and $A_2$, then if $\theta_1$ is a dominant platform for the 1$^{st}$ population and $\theta_2$ is a dominant strategy for the 2$^{nd}$ population, the vector $\overline{\theta}$, which is composed of the first in components of $\theta_1$, and the last $r = n - m$ components of $\theta_2$, is a dominant strategy for the general election.

This theorem has a rather intuitive interpretation. Given that one of the mutually exclusive and exhaustive groups "desires" one set of policies, that the other group "desires" another set of policies, and that there is no conflict between the two sets of policies since each refers to a mutually exclusive set of issues, then the politician can enhance his chance of winning the election by giving each group just what it desires.

## 7. Concluding Comments

No attempt is made here to summarize the results which were derived in this analysis. Yet, some of the remarks of the introduction merit repetition. There is no claim that this simple model of policy formation captures the anomalies of the modern, complex, political phenomenon. Simplifying assumptions were made to reduce the problem to a manageable size so that certain propositions could be established. It is hoped that these propositions (as well as the analysis itself) produce insights into the complexities of policy formation in a democratic society.

One additional remark is warranted. It is clear that certain complications, such as multi-party competition under various conditions, can be introduced and analyzed within the broad framework developed here. These additional complications, as well as the relaxing of certain of the assumptions, must await the results of future efforts.

FIGURE 1

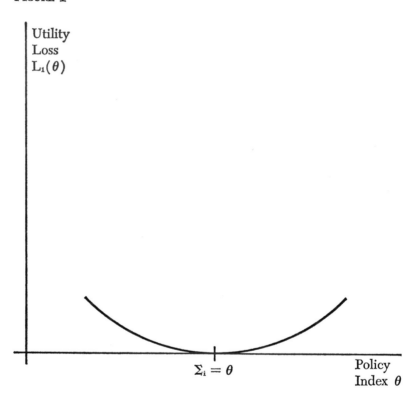

FIGURE 2

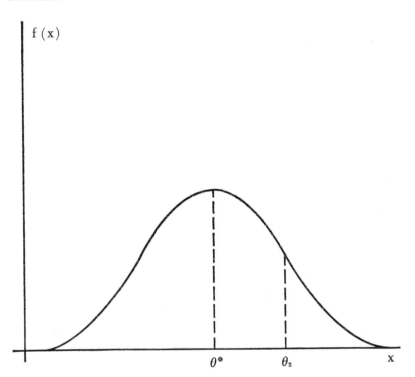

FIGURE 3

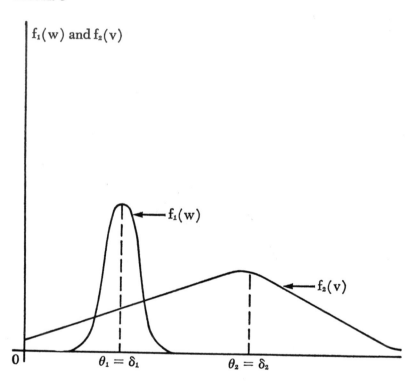